Getty-Dubay®
ITALIC HANDWRITING SERIES

Book A
Basic Italic

Fourth Edition

by
Barbara Getty & Inga Dubay

GETTY-DUBAY® ITALIC HANDWRITING SERIES

BOOK A ▪ Basic Italic
14 mm body height

BOOK B ▪ Basic Italic
11 mm body height, 9 mm

BOOK C ▪ Basic & Cursive Italic
9 mm, 6 mm body height   Introduction to Cursive Italic

BOOK D ▪ Basic & Cursive Italic
6 mm, 5 mm body height

BOOK E ▪ Basic & Cursive Italic
6 mm, 5 mm, 4 mm body height

BOOK F ▪ Basic & Cursive Italic
6 mm, 5 mm, 4 mm body height

BOOK G ▪ Basic & Cursive Italic
5 mm, 4 mm body height

INSTRUCTION MANUAL

BOOK A ▪ FOURTH EDITION
Copyright 2012 by Barbara M. Getty and Inga S. Dubay
ISBN 978-0-9827762-3-0

THIRD EDITION
Copyright 1994 by Barbara M. Getty and Inga S. Dubay
SECOND EDITION
Copyright 1986 by Barbara M. Getty and Inga S. Dubay
REVISED EDITION
Copyright 1980 by Barbara M. Getty and Inga S. Dubay
FIRST EDITION
Copyright 1979 by Barbara M. Getty and Inga S. Dubay

Fourth printing 2021

Published by Handwriting Success, LLC, Portland, Oregon U

Distributed by Allport Editions ▪ www.allport.com
716 NE Lawrence Avenue, Portland, Oregon 97232 USA

Printed with low-VOC inks. Interior papers contain sustainable-harvest wood
fibers and a minimum 10% post-consumer waste. Printed in the United States of Am

Cover Design: Sinda Markham
Front cover picture: Flowers of the sunflower family in the Ochoco National Forest, Or
Back cover pictures: Columbine flower, Golden-mantled squirrel

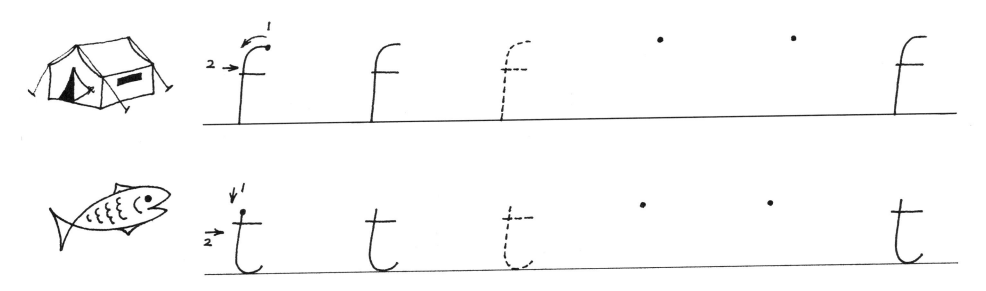

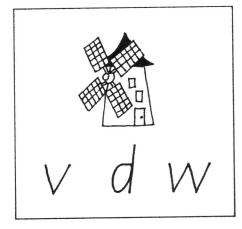

b c l

m k y

s n e

v d w

TOP TWO LINES: Ask the student to draw a line from the picture to the letter that stands for the correct beginning sound.

BOTTOM FOUR SQUARES: Ask the student to circle the letter that stands for the beginning sound of the picture.

Getty-Dubay® Italic Handwriting Series · Book A

CONTENTS

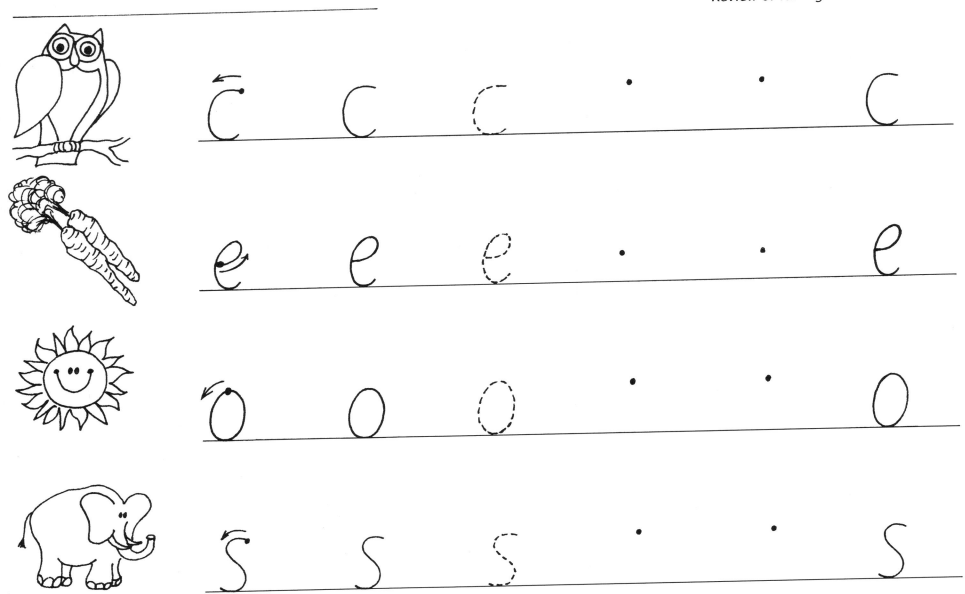

c c c · · c

e e e · · e

o o o · · o

s s s · · s

Ask the student to draw a line from the picture to the letter that stands for the correct beginning sound.

INTRODUCTION

This is the first of seven workbooks providing instruction in basic italic handwriting. It is designed for the beginning student of handwriting and is recommended for preschool, kindergarten and/or early first grade (5 to 7 years of age).

The twenty-six lowercase letters and the twenty-six capitals are introduced one letter per page. Letters are arranged in the order of lowercase families, which group letters with similar strokes together and progress from simple to more complex forms. The matching capital letter occurs on the reverse of each lowercase page allowing introduction of both lowercase and capital together if preferred.

Each page is designed for the student to trace the models provided, write letters at the given dots, and to write a "best" letter in the empty box on each alphabet page. The standard writing tool is the pencil although other writing instruments such as the fiber tip pen may be used. When students are ready, they should trace the word describing the illustration on each letter page, following the dots and arrows.

It is essential that the instructor provide an understanding of the dot and the arrow to assist the writer in completing the pages successfully. The self-assessment method used in the *Getty-Dubay® Italic Handwriting Series* enables students to monitor their individual progress. Step 1, LOOK, of the three-step LOOK, PLAN, PRACTICE format, is incorporated on 21 of the student pages. Students are asked to "LOOK" at their writing and affirm what is best. On the 21 pages with "LOOK" questions, students should circle their chosen answers. See INSTRUCTION MANUAL, pp. 13, 18 & 19.

The *Getty-Dubay® Italic Handwriting Series* INSTRUCTION MANUAL is to be used in conjunction with this workbook. Explanations and in-depth descriptions of lowercase letters, capitals, joins, and numerals are presented in the manual, emphasizing shape, strokes, size, slope and spacing of the letters Also included in the manual are: a rationale for italic handwriting, techniques for teaching and assessing handwriting, sequence of skills, handwriting activities, and a brief history of our alphabet.

BOOK B, basic italic, follows this workbook and is designed for the beginning reader. In the third book, BOOK C, basic italic letterforms are reinforced and cursive italic is introduced. BOOKS D, E, F, and G provide a complete basic italic and cursive italic handwriting program. BOOKS B, C, and/or D may also be suitable for the person learning English as a second language.

The format of this book was chosen to accommodate both the left- and right-handed writer. When open, the book fits easily on a small desk, and the writer is not encumbered with an additional page to the left or right. From day one, use a Getty-Dubay® basic italic desk strip as a reminder. Blackline masters are designed for supplementary practice and are available for each workbook in the series. See www.handwritingsuccess.com for these supplementary materials.

You can guide children toward the challenge and delight in the writing process by reading to them, modeling handwriting, providing writing materials, and especially by building enthusiasm for the letters of our alphabet and for the written word.

· abcdefghijklmnopqrstuvwxyz ·

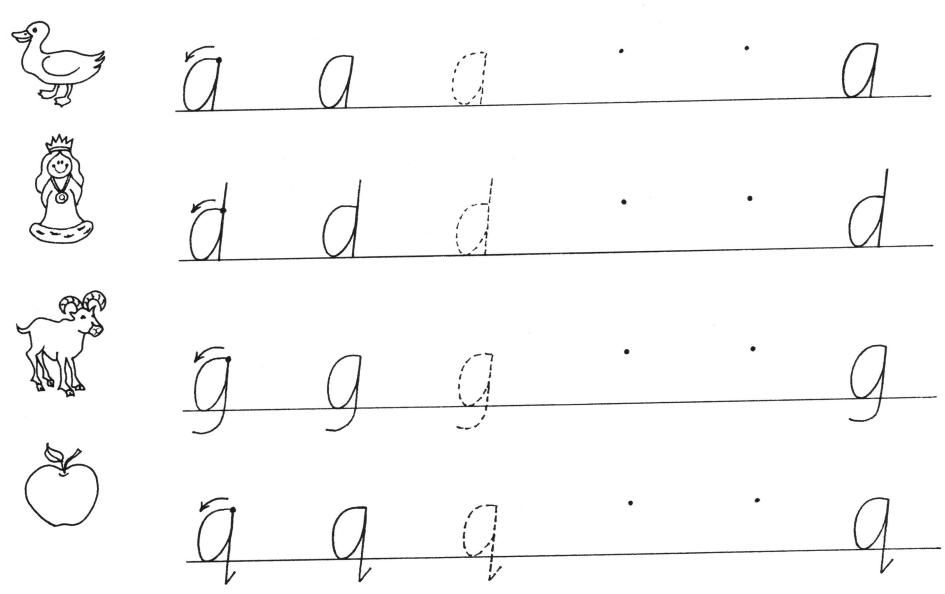

Ask the student to draw a line from the picture to the letter that stands for the correct beginning sound.

GETTY-DUBAY® HANDWRITING REMINDERS

PENCIL HOLD

Hold the pencil with the thumb and index finger, resting it on the middle finger. Rest the shaft of the pencil near the large knuckle. Hold the tool firmly and avoid pinching. To relax the hand, tap index finger on the pencil three times. Avoid "thumb wrap" and a "death grip".

PAPER POSITION

LEFT-HANDED: If the left-handed student writes with the wrist below the writing line, turn paper clockwise so it is slanted to the right, as illustrated.

If the left-handed student writes with a hook, with the wrist above the writing line, turn the paper counter-clockwise so it is slanted to the left, as illustrated. (Similar to right-handed position)

RIGHT-HANDED: If the student is right-handed, turn paper counter-clockwise so it is slanted to the left, as illustrated.

POSTURE

Rest feet flat on the floor and keep back comfortably straight without slumping. Rest forearms on writing surface. The student holds workbook or paper with the nonwriting hand so that the writing area is centered in the front of the student.

PRACTICE PAPER

Book A—Use unlined or lined paper together with workbooks.

MATERIALS

The *Getty-Dubay® Italic Handwriting Series* workbooks, BOOKS A-G, and the INSTRUCTION MANUAL constitute a step-by-step program. Related materials consist of:

1. BLACKLINE MASTERS/WORKSHEETS - half sheets for introduction to, or review of, workbook pages.
2. CLASSROOM WALL CHARTS - basic & cursive italic.
3. DESK STRIPS - basic & cursive italic.

VOCABULARY

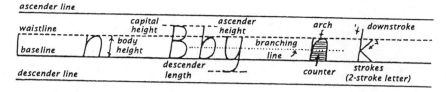

DIRECT INSTRUCTION

Several sessions of direct instruction each week are essential for a successful program. BOOK A – 5 to 10 minute sessions a day are recommended, see INSTRUCTION MANUAL, pp. 18-19

- SHAPE & STROKE SEQUENCE – teach basic italic in letter family groups, or according to the reading program in grade 1.
- SLOPE – encourage a consistent letter slope. Vertical letters (0° slope) may be the easiest to teach to beginning writers.
- SIZE – At first, allow students to write letters any size they wish on unlined paper, then introduce the workbook. A recommended progression through this book is one letter (lowercase and/or capital) per week.

SPACING

When young students are writing words, at first have them leave a space about the width of their two small fingers between words. As they become more proficient, they can leave less space.

ASSESSMENT

The *Getty-Dubay® Italic Handwriting Series* provides a self-assessment process, LOOK, PLAN, PRACTICE, to enable the student to monitor progress. LOOK, step 1 of this process begins on some of the student pages in BOOK A. Assessment is the key to improving handwriting; in this book we introduce the first of three steps in the LOOK, PLAN, PRACTICE self-assessment process. The students look at their own writing and answer any questions on the page. The pencil indicates the student is to make a written response, generally by circling "yes" or "no". The teacher may encourage students to award themselves a star or a smiling face at the top of the page when they notice self-improvement.

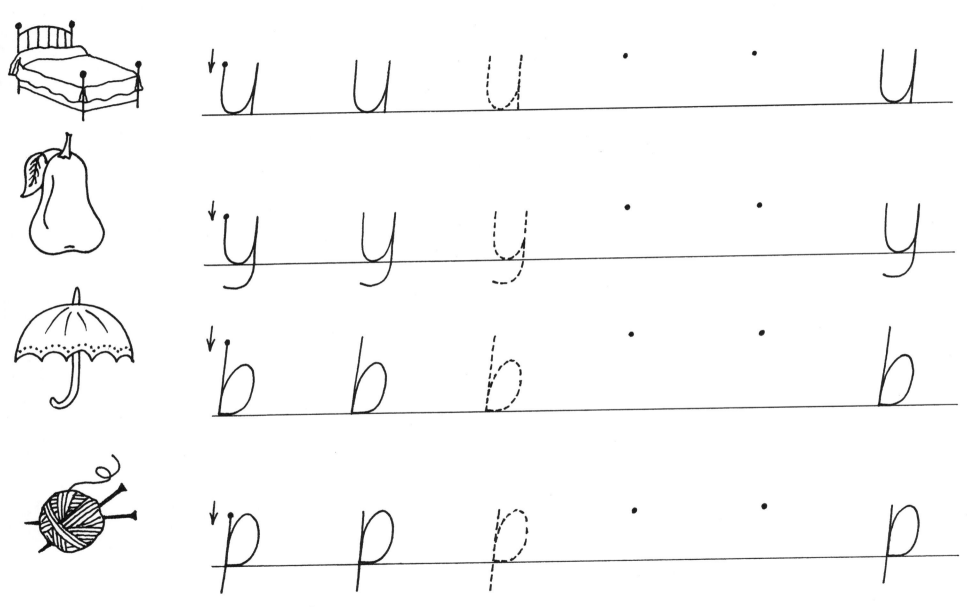

Ask the student to draw a line from the picture to the letter
that stands for the correct beginning sound.

All letters written in one stroke unless otherwise indicated.

All letters start at the top except lowercase **d** and **e**.

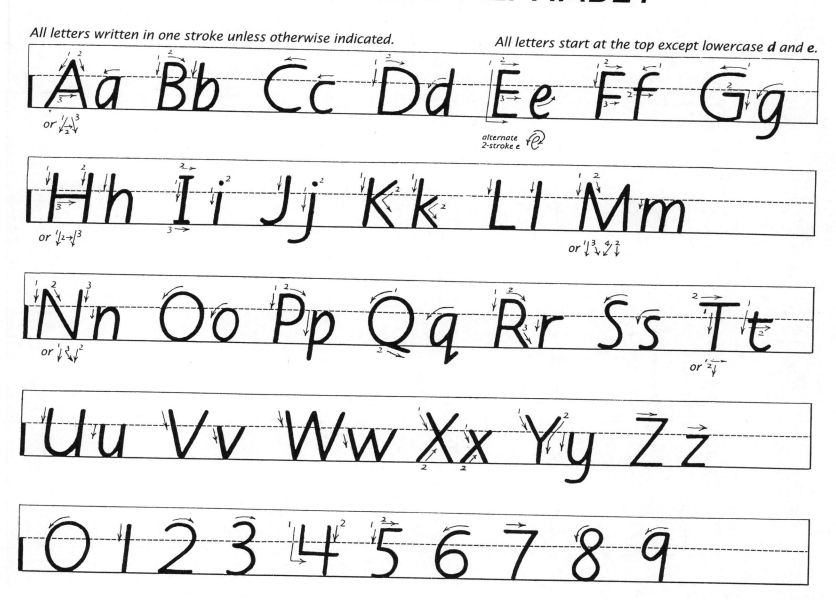

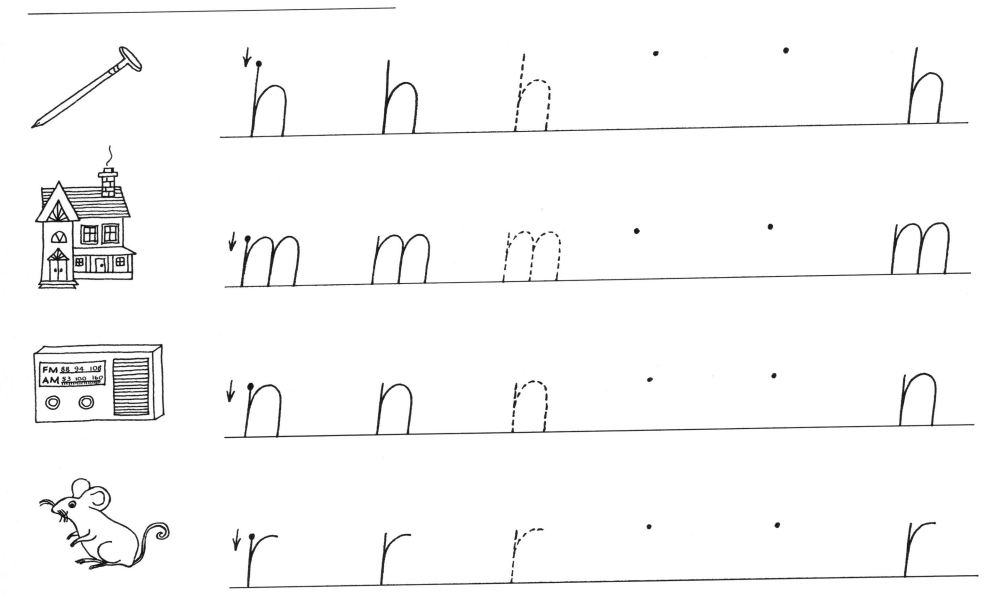

*Ask the student to draw a line from the picture to the letter
that stands for the correct beginning sound.*

THE BEGINNING WRITER

Learning how to write involves much more than learning to write letters. It is a sophisticated, complex process involving learning letterforms, learning how to space within and between words, and learning how to organize writing on a page. Research indicates that there exists an almost perfect correlation between measures evaluating the children's *awareness* of their fingers and the ability to *use* their fingers in precise manual skills.

Ways to determine manual ability

To assist young students increase awareness of their hands and fingers, and to help you, the teacher, evaluate students' manual skills, have your students perform these tasks:

1. Direct the students to touch each of their fingers to their thumb, in order, from the first to the little finger. (By the age of six years, most children should be able to complete this exercise using one or both hands at a time.)

2. Have the students connect two dots that are spaced approximately eight inches apart on a page. (Most children of five years can accomplish this. However, if the student draws beyond the second dot or draws an unusually shaky line when nearing the second dot, it may indicate potential deficiencies in handwriting skills.)

Ways to improve kinesthetic perception of the hands

1. Unstructured clay modeling facilitates a student's perception of his or her hands. Encourage the student to manipulate the clay in every possible way—squeezing, flattening, poking, making shapes, etc.

2. To heighten the student's perception of shape, use a box in which a variety of small objects are placed for the student to feel but not see.

   a. Ask the student to reach in the box and find an unseen object that matches the one he or she is looking at.

   b. Direct the student to locate in the box an object that you or another student has described.

   c. Ask the student to find two objects with similar characteristics— two fuzzy objects, two heavy objects, two small objects, etc.

3. Draw several circles on a sheet of paper. To determine the student's ability to aim the finger and hand and also to point, have the student place dots in the circles with a pencil, pen, or crayon. Vary the difficulty of this task by increasing or decreasing the size of the circles or increasing the rate at which the dots are made. (The student must be able to point at a given or imaginary point in order to begin the stroke of a letter.)

Ways to confirm hand-eye tracking skills

The ability to control continuous hand movements while drawing lines of varying difficulty is basic to handwriting. If you are able to detect problems as the student completes the following tasks and are able to obtain appropriate assistance for the student, subsequent difficulties may be avoided.

1. Demonstrate drawing parallel lines. Then direct the student to draw parallel lines of a given length, first at a relaxed pace then at a faster one.

2. Direct the student to draw two curved lines equal in distance from one another. Later require more difficult shapes that combine straight lines, angles, and/or curves.

3. Direct the student to connect numbered dots on a sheet of paper that require horizontal, vertical and lateral movements. Place the paper in front of the student, close to the dominant hand. Later, space the dots further apart and require the student to cross the midline of his or her body. This latter task may cause the neuro-logically challenged student some difficulty.

The above evaluative tasks may be of help in assisting the learning of handwriting and in discovering deficiencies.

(See INSTRUCTION MANUAL, p. 13, for more suggestions concerning the beginning writer.)

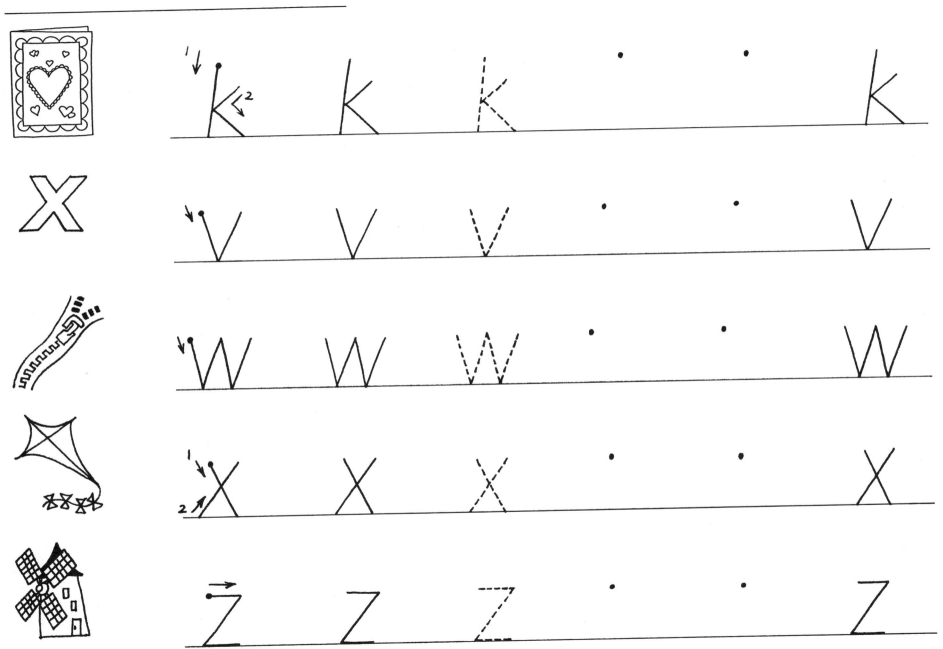

Ask the student to draw a line from the picture to the letter
that stands for the correct beginning sound.

60

BASIC SHAPES

Before the student begins writing in BOOK A, the authors recommend that the student practice the following shapes on unlined paper, one shape at a time. Allow the student to write each shape any size at first. Later, ask the student to write very large and very small forms of that same shape. We suggest the student also practice these shapes on a chalkboard and/or in cornmeal. (See INSTRUCTION MANUAL, "Activity," pp. 35 & 41.)

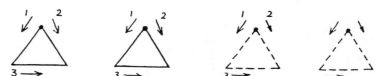

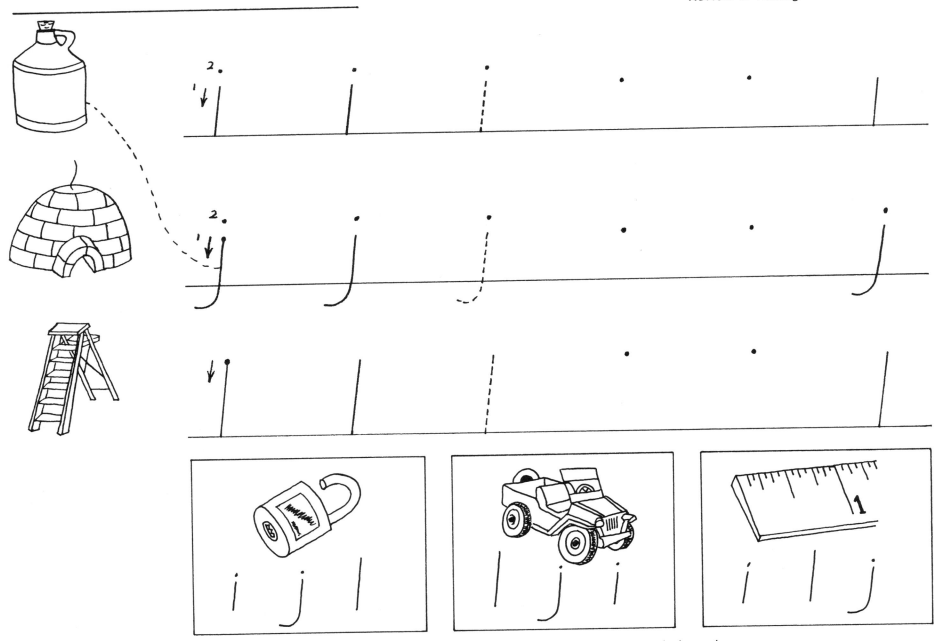

TOP THREE LINES: Ask the student to draw a line from the picture to the letter that stands for the correct beginning sound.

BOTTOM THREE BOXES: Ask the student to circle the letter that stands for the beginning sound of the picture.

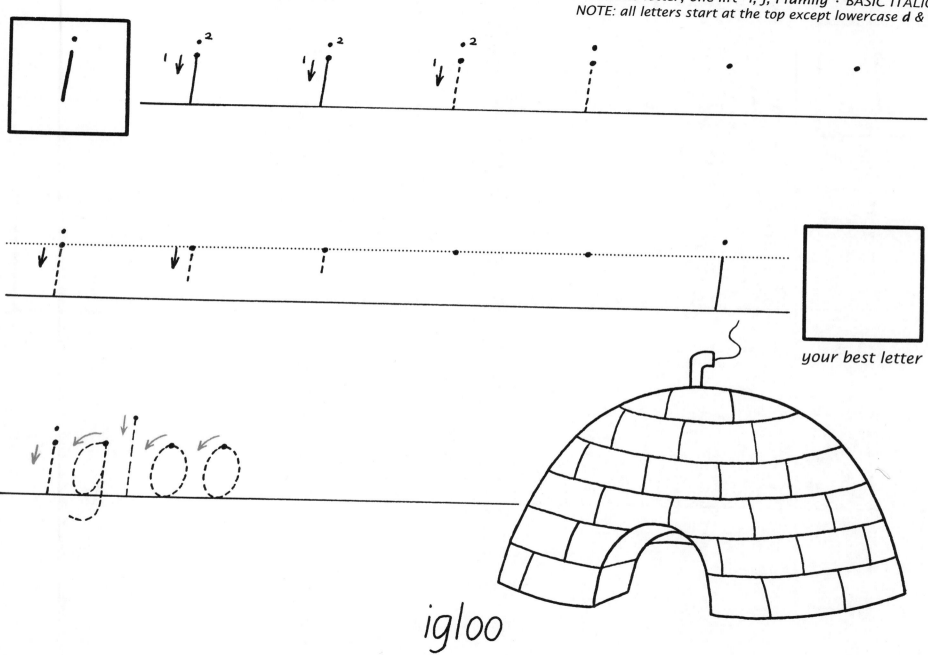

two stroke letter, one lift i, j, l family · BASIC ITALIC
NOTE: all letters start at the top except lowercase *d & e*

i

your best letter

igloo

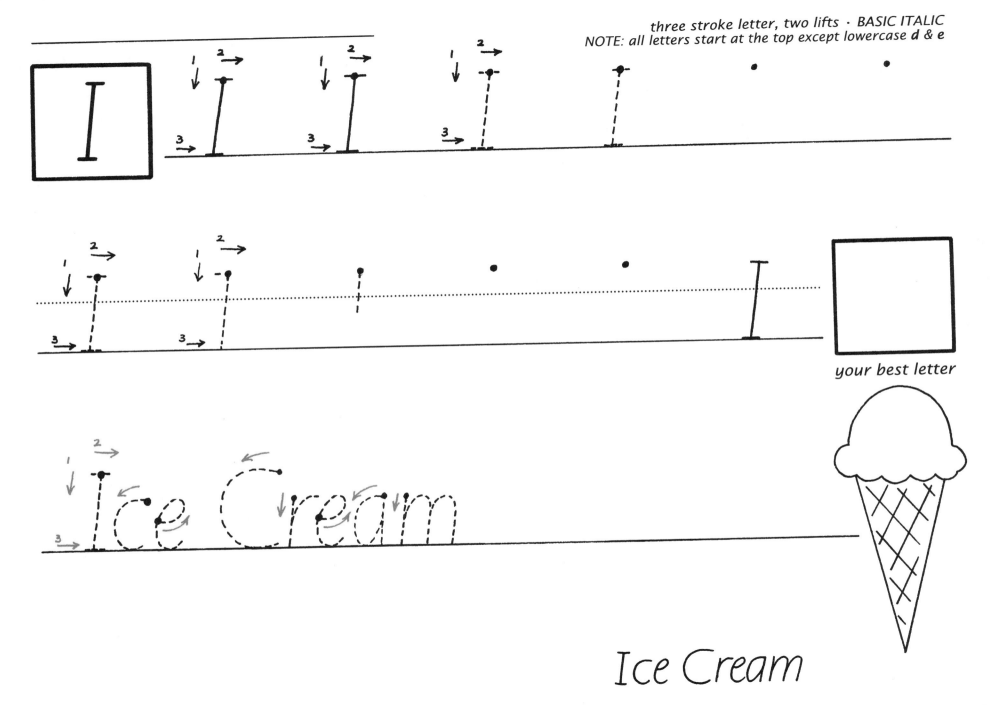

your best letter

Ice Cream

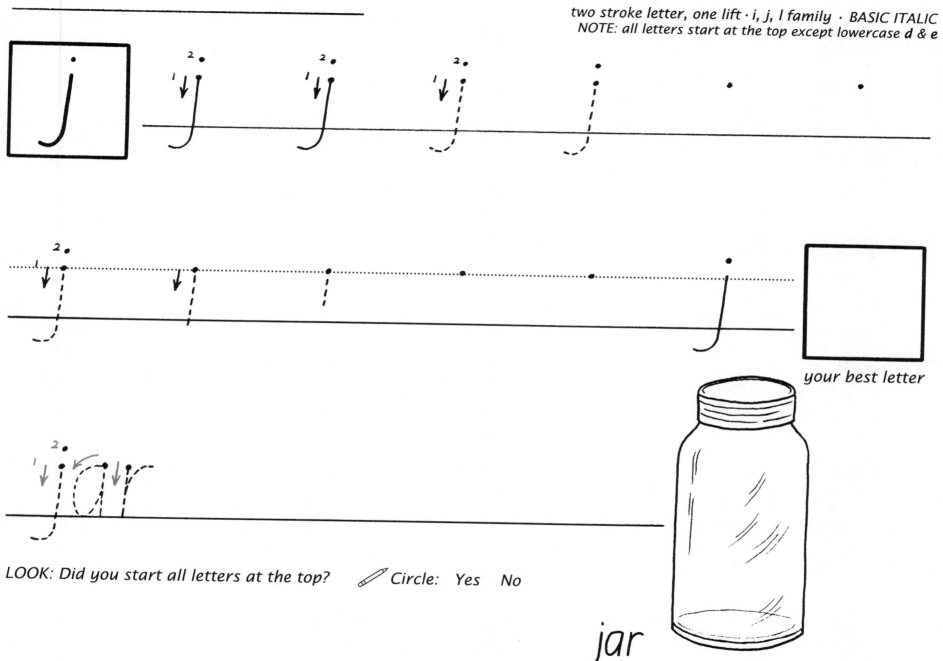

two stroke letter, one lift · i, j, l family · BASIC ITALIC
NOTE: all letters start at the top except lowercase **d** & **e**

j

your best letter

LOOK: Did you start all letters at the top? ✎ Circle: Yes No

jar

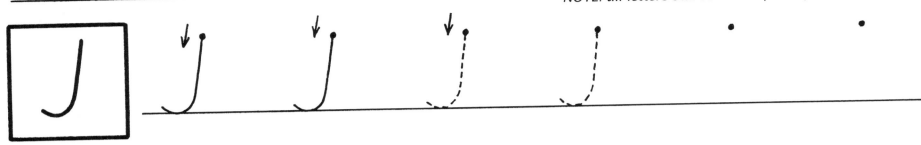

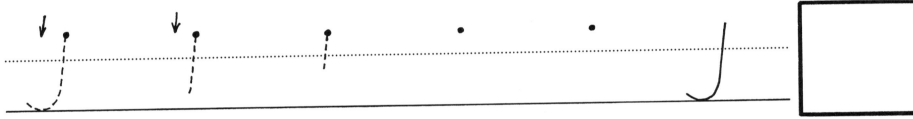

your best letter

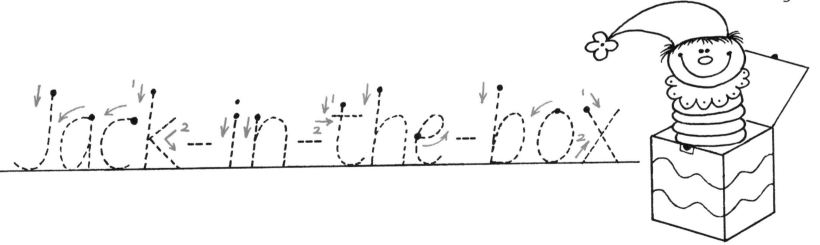

Jack-in-the-box

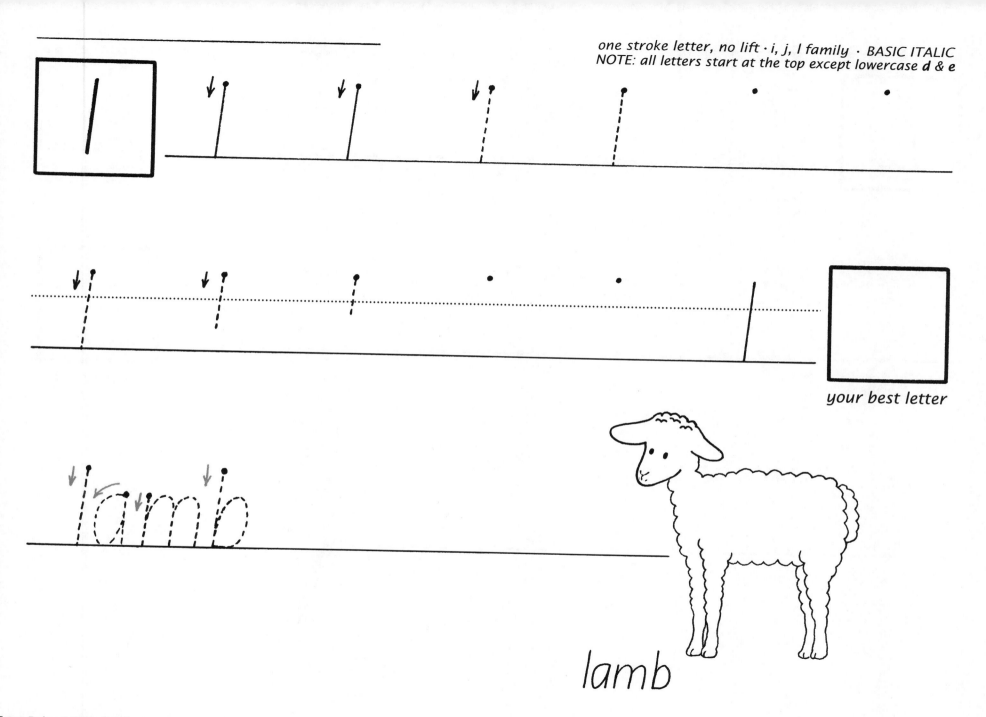

one stroke letter, no lift · *i, j, l* family · BASIC ITALIC
NOTE: all letters start at the top except lowercase **d** & **e**

your best letter

lamb

your best letter

Lock

Getty-Dubay® Italic Handwriting Series · Book A

© 2012 Getty-Dubay

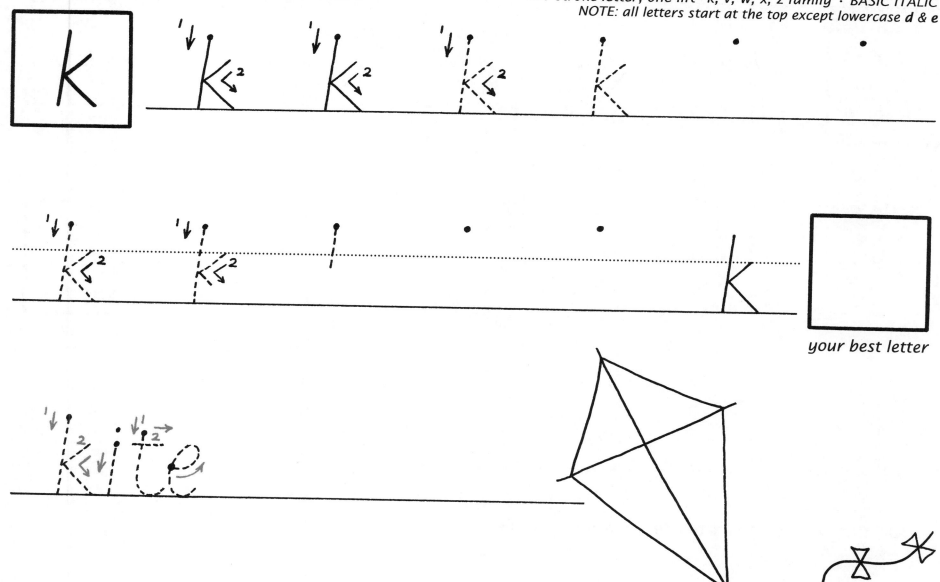

two stroke letter, one lift · k, v, w, x, z family · BASIC ITALIC
NOTE: all letters start at the top except lowercase *d* & *e*

your best letter

kite

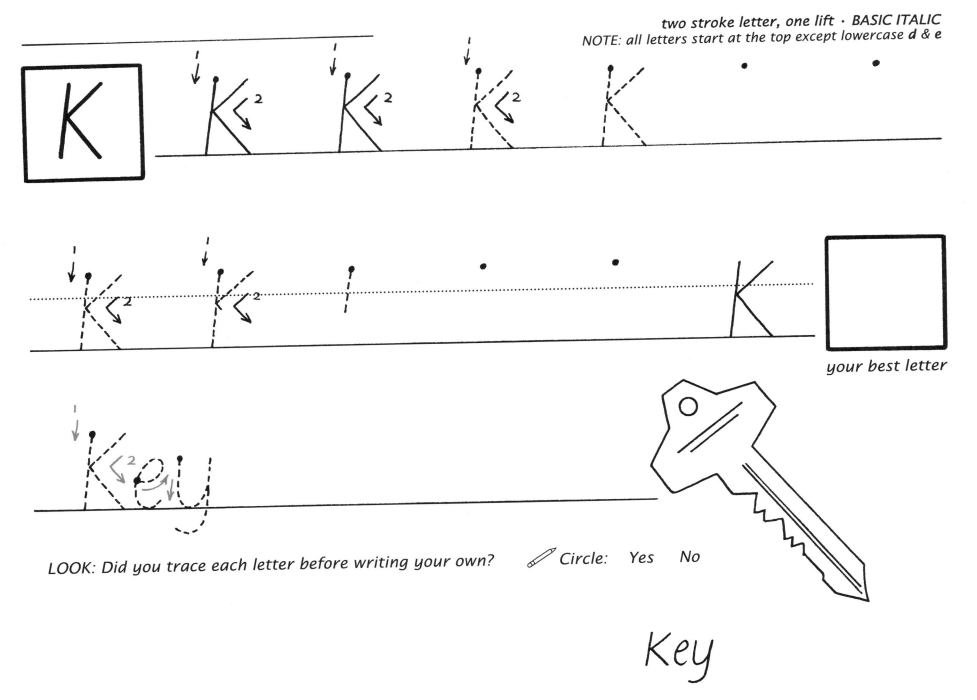

your best letter

LOOK: Did you trace each letter before writing your own?   Circle: Yes   No

Key

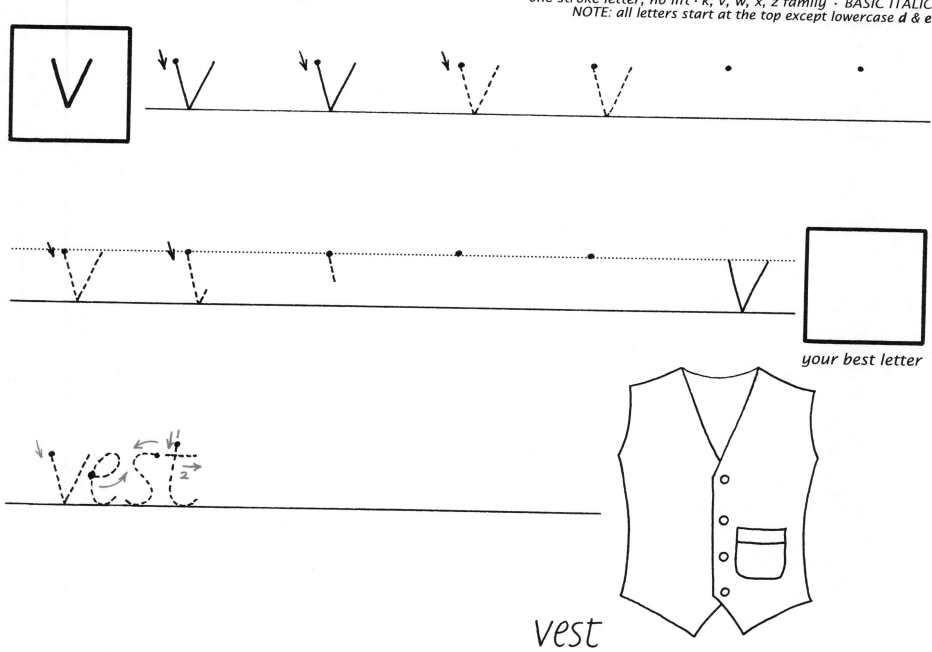

one stroke letter, no lift · k, v, w, x, z family · BASIC ITALIC
NOTE: all letters start at the top except lowercase *d & e*

your best letter

vest

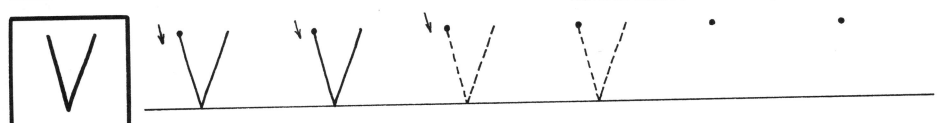

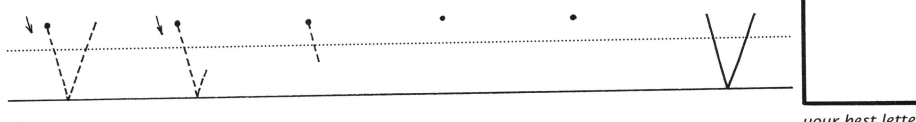

your best letter

LOOK: Did you start all letters at the top except **e**? ✏ Circle: Yes   No

Valentine

54

one stroke letter, no lift · k, v, w, x, z family · BASIC ITALIC
NOTE: all letters start at the top except lowercase *d* & *e*

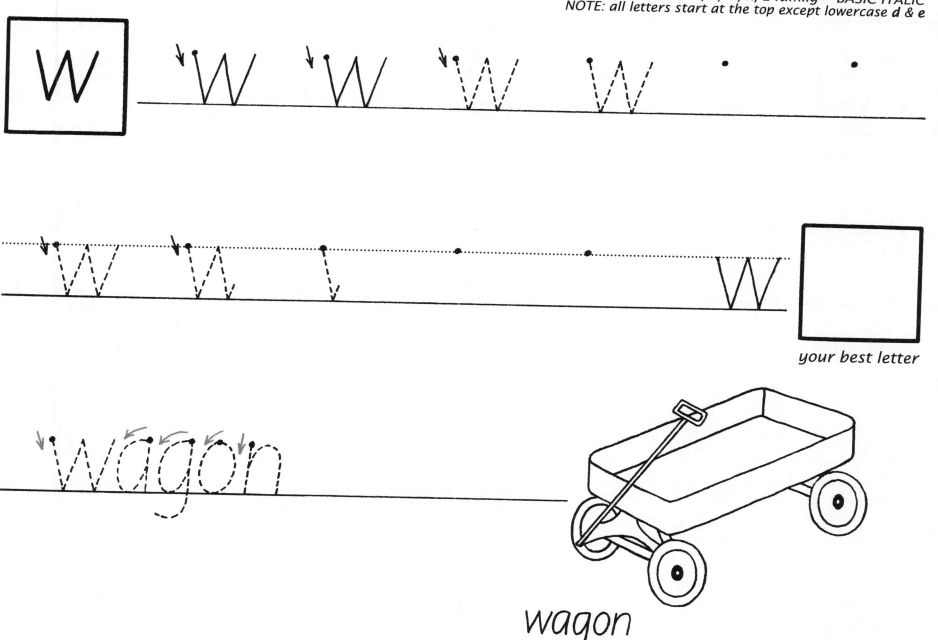

your best letter

wagon

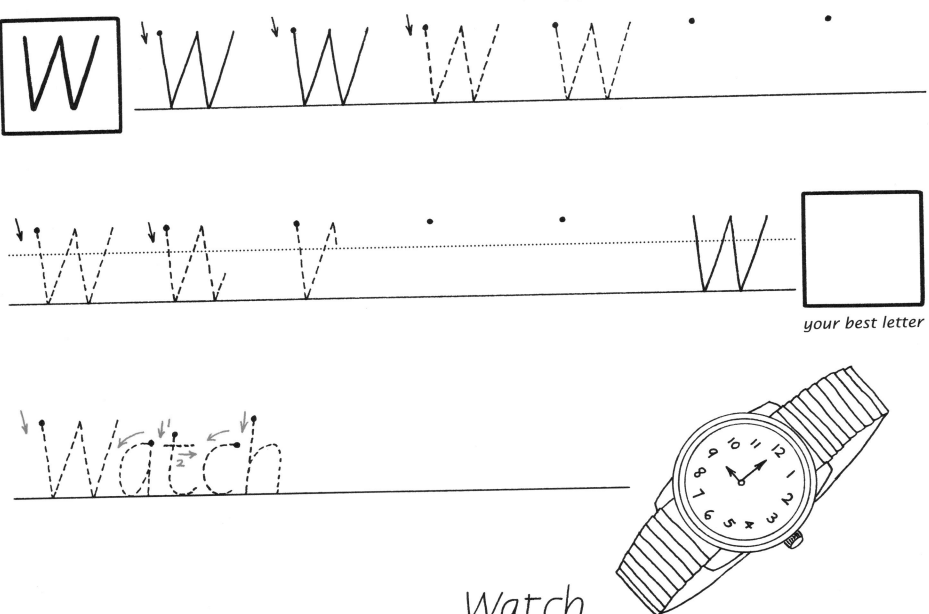

your best letter

Watch

Getty-Dubay® Italic Handwriting Series · Book A

© 2012 Getty-Dubay

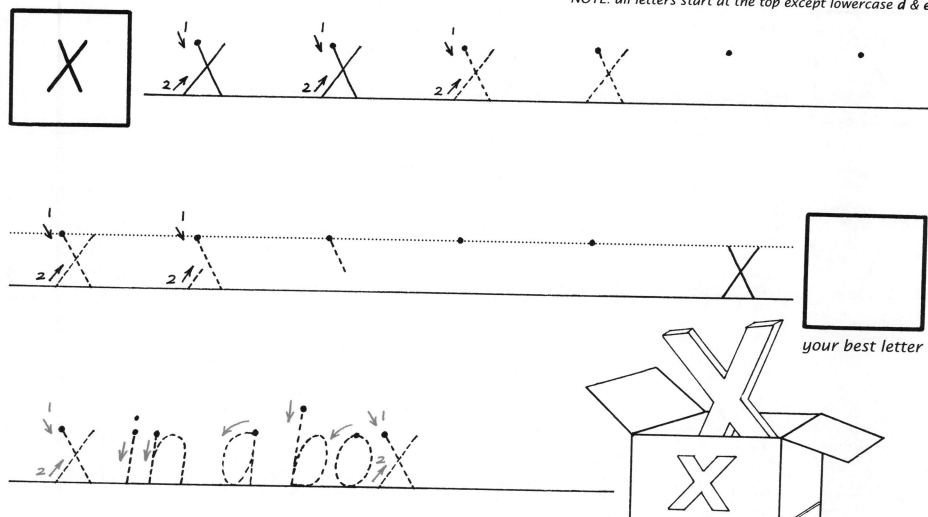

your best letter

x in a box

NOTE: all letters start at the top except lowercase **d** & **e**

X

X X X X

X

your best letter

X on a box

X on a box

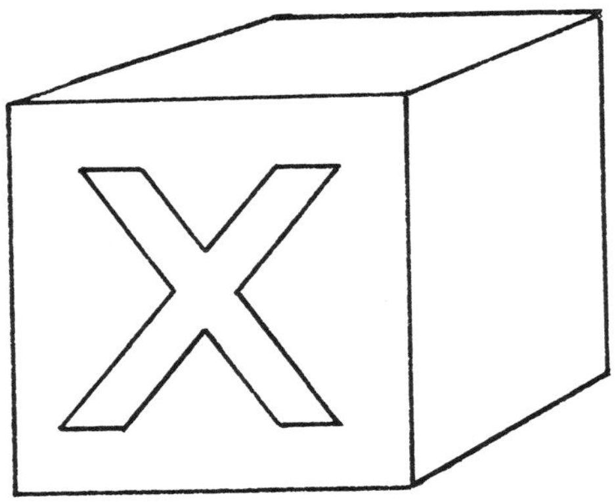

one stroke letter, no lift · k, v, w, x, z family · BASIC ITALIC
NOTE: all letters start at the top except lowercase *d* & *e*

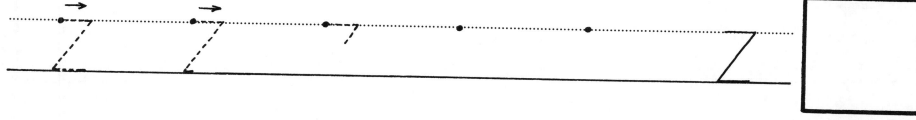

your best letter

LOOK: Did you trace each letter before writing your own?

✏ Circle: Yes   No

zebra

one stroke letter, no lift · BASIC ITALIC
NOTE: all letters start at the top except lowercase **d** & **e**

Z

your best letter

Zipper

Zipper

Getty-Dubay® Italic Handwriting Series · Book A

© 2012 Getty-Dubay

h

your best letter

helicopter

helicopter

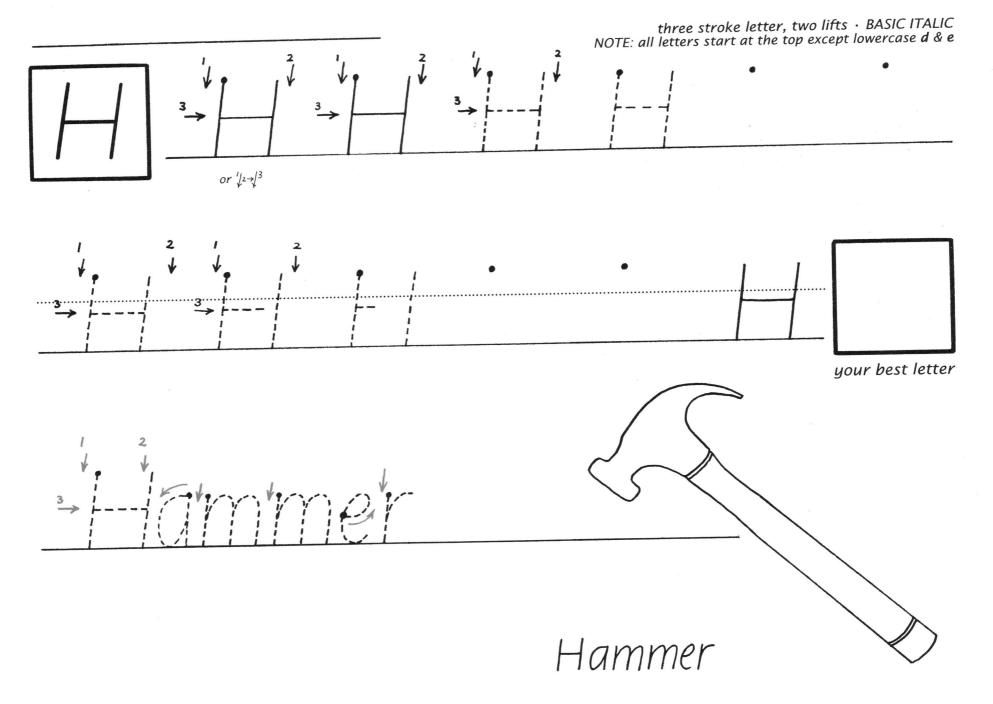

or ¹⁄₂ →|³

your best letter

Hammer

m

m m m m m

m m m m m

your best letter

mouse

LOOK: Did you start all letters at the top except *e*? ✏ Circle: Yes   No

mouse

M

or ↓¹³↓ ²↓⁴↓

M M M M M M · ·

m m i · · M M

your best letter

Mittens

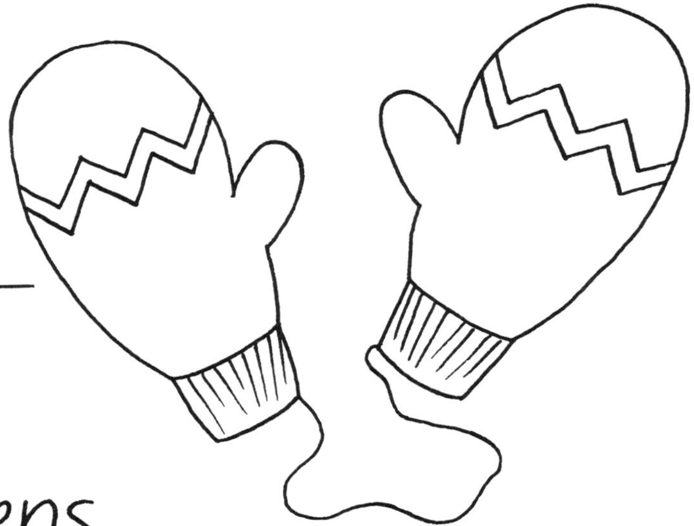

Mittens

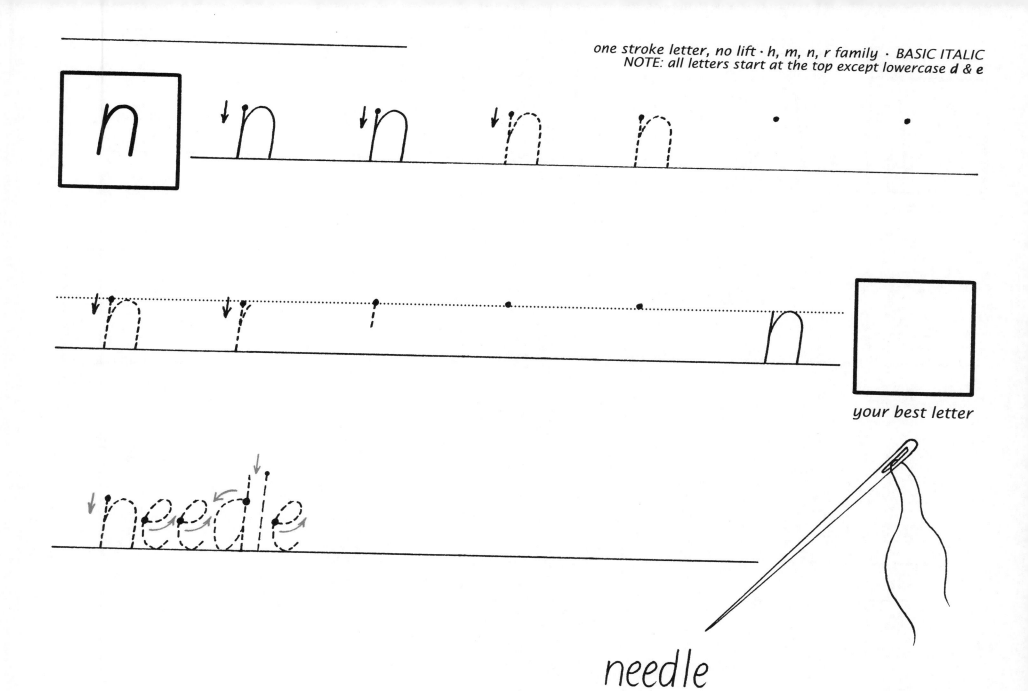

your best letter

needle

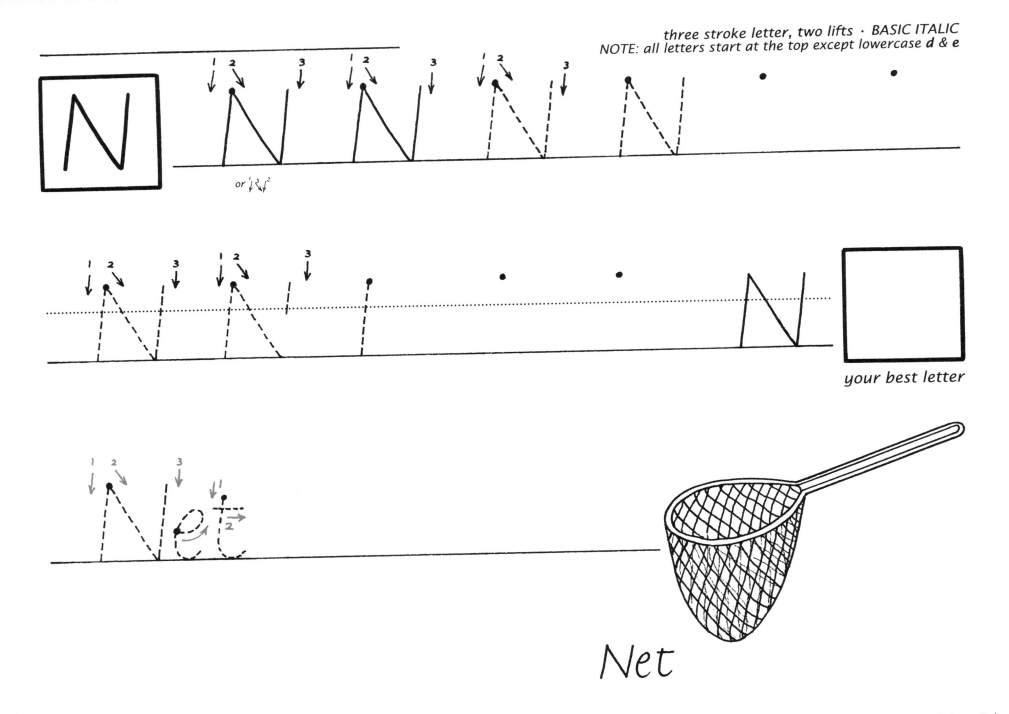

or

your best letter

Net

r

your best letter

rabbit

LOOK: Did you start each letter at the top?   Circle: Yes   No

rabbit

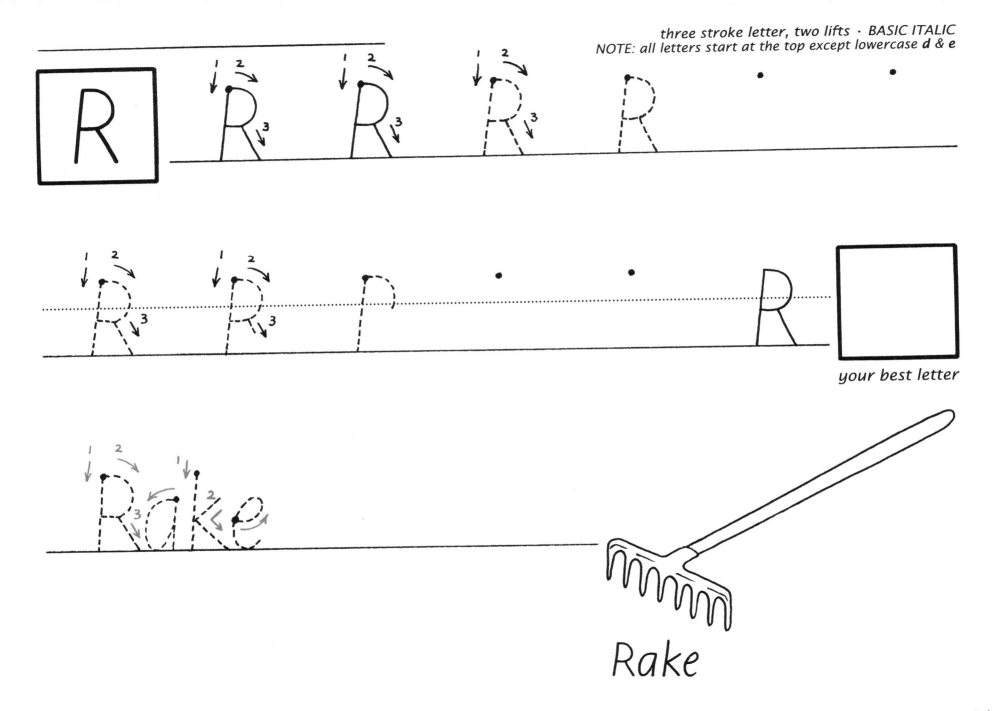

your best letter

Rake

47

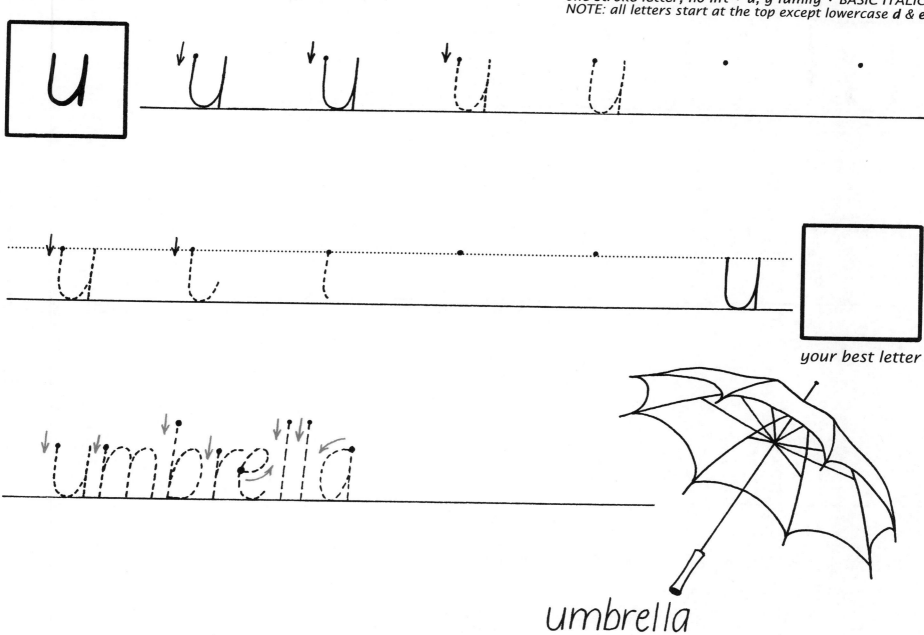

one stroke letter, no lift · **u, y** family · BASIC ITALIC
NOTE: all letters start at the top except lowercase **d & e**

your best letter

umbrella

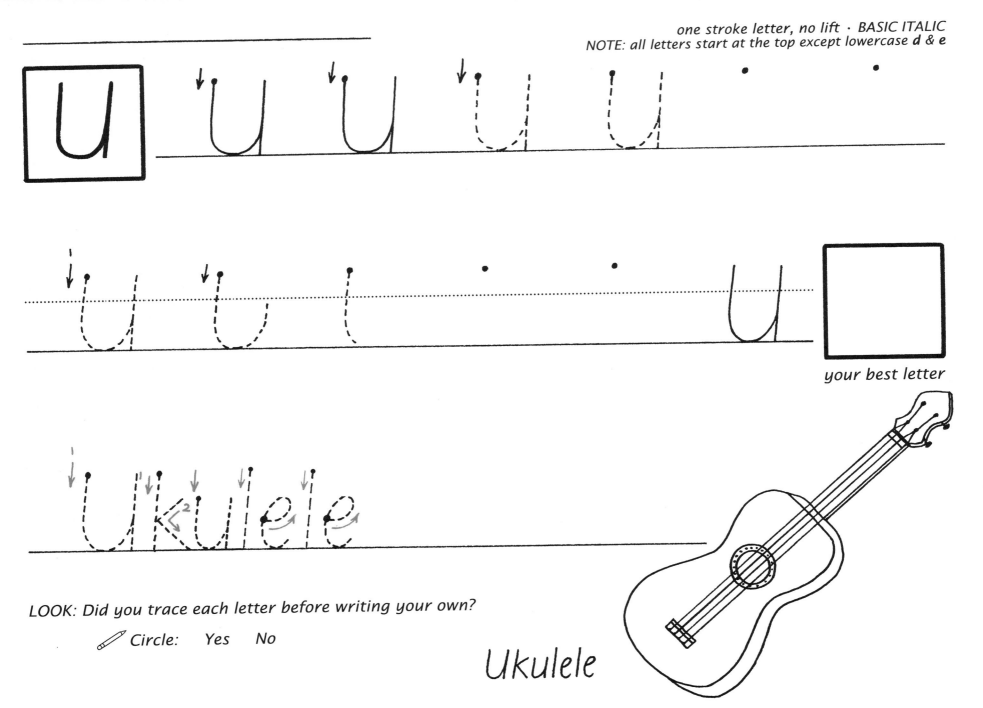

your best letter

LOOK: *Did you trace each letter before writing your own?*

✏ Circle: Yes   No

Ukulele

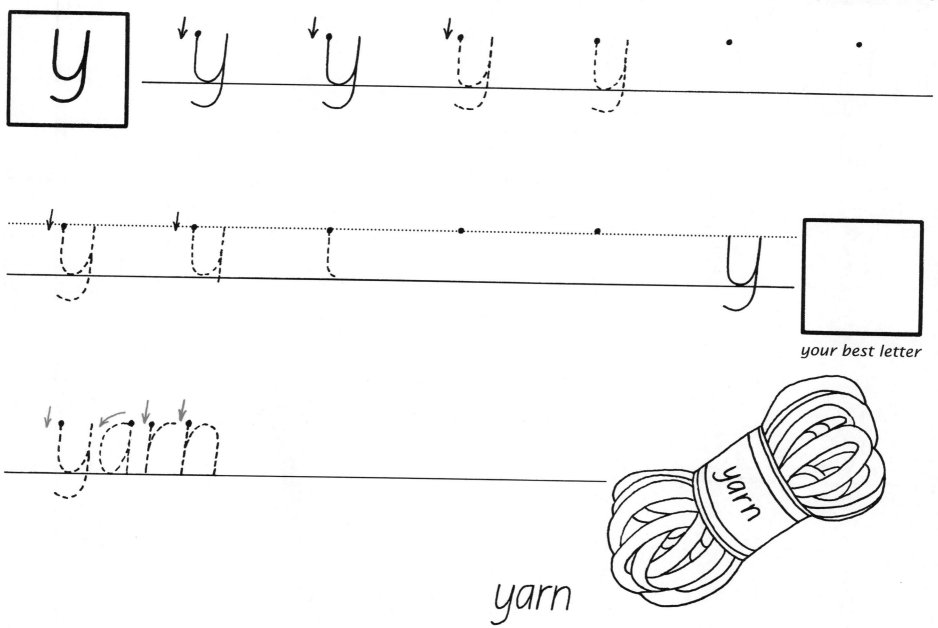

your best letter

yarn

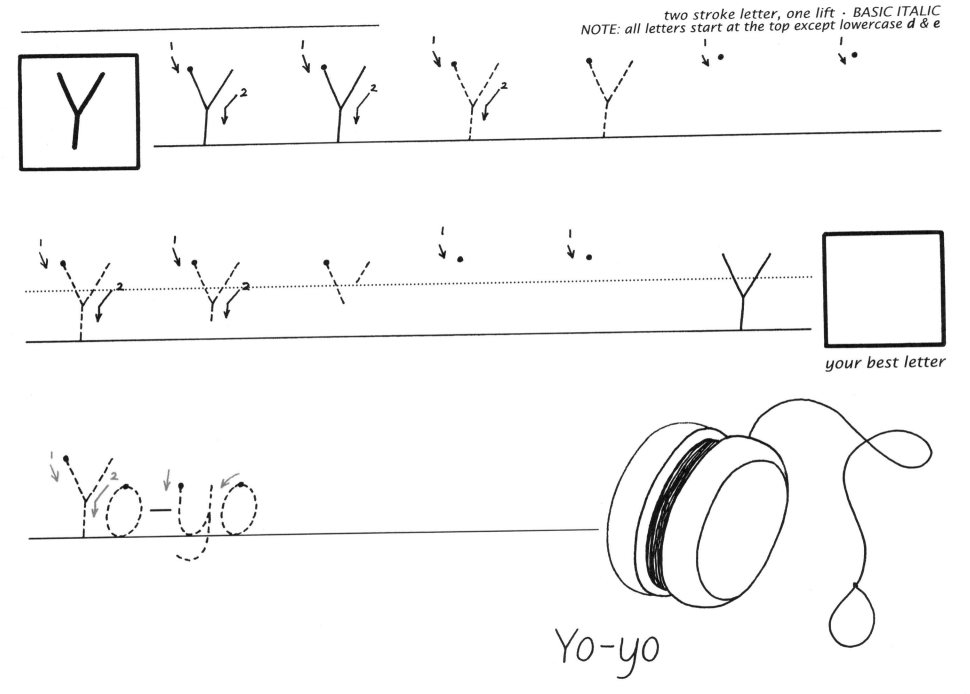

your best letter

Yo-yo

your best letter

LOOK: Did you close each **a** at the top? Circle: Yes   No

apple

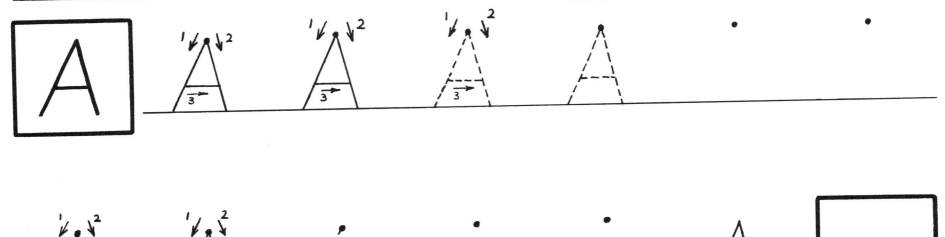

your best letter

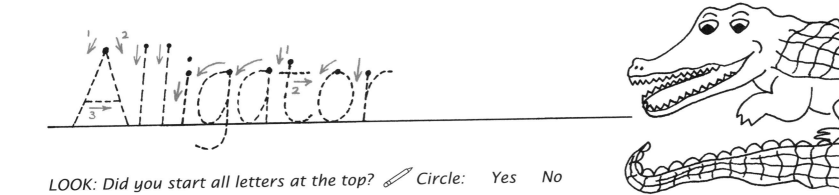

LOOK: Did you start all letters at the top? ✏ Circle:　　Yes　　No

Alligator

one stroke letter, no lift · *a, d, g, q* family · BASIC ITALIC
NOTE: all letters start at the top except lowercase *d & e*

d

your best letter

dog

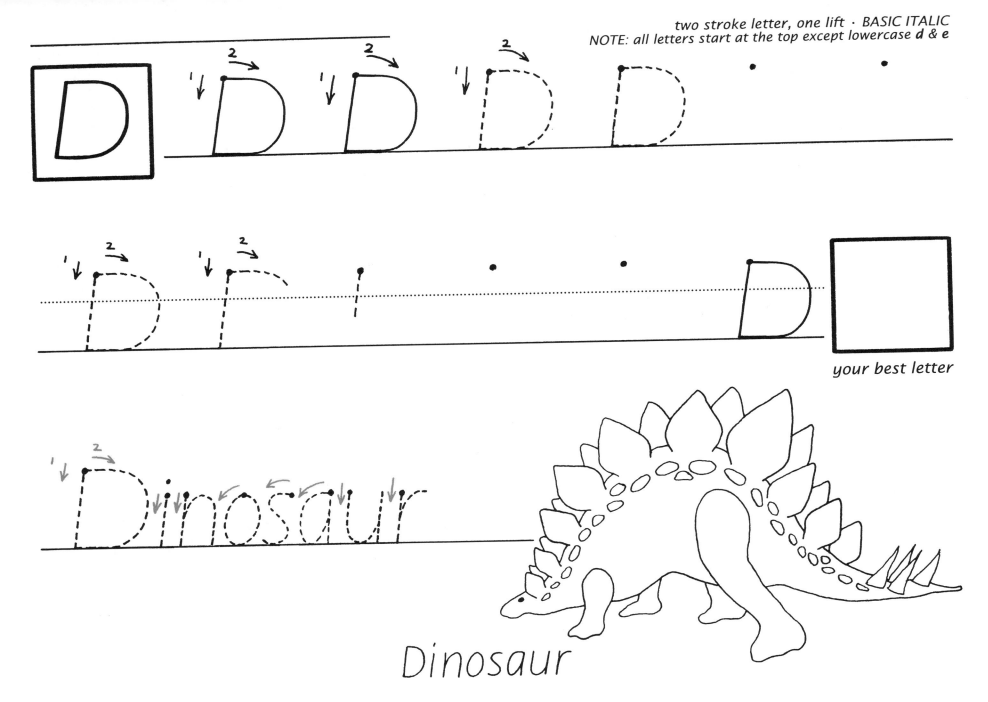

two stroke letter, one lift · BASIC ITALIC
NOTE: all letters start at the top except lowercase *d* & *e*

your best letter

Dinosaur

Getty-Dubay® Italic Handwriting Series · Book A

your best letter

LOOK: Did you trace each letter before writing your own?　　Circle:　Yes　No

goat

G

your best letter

Gate

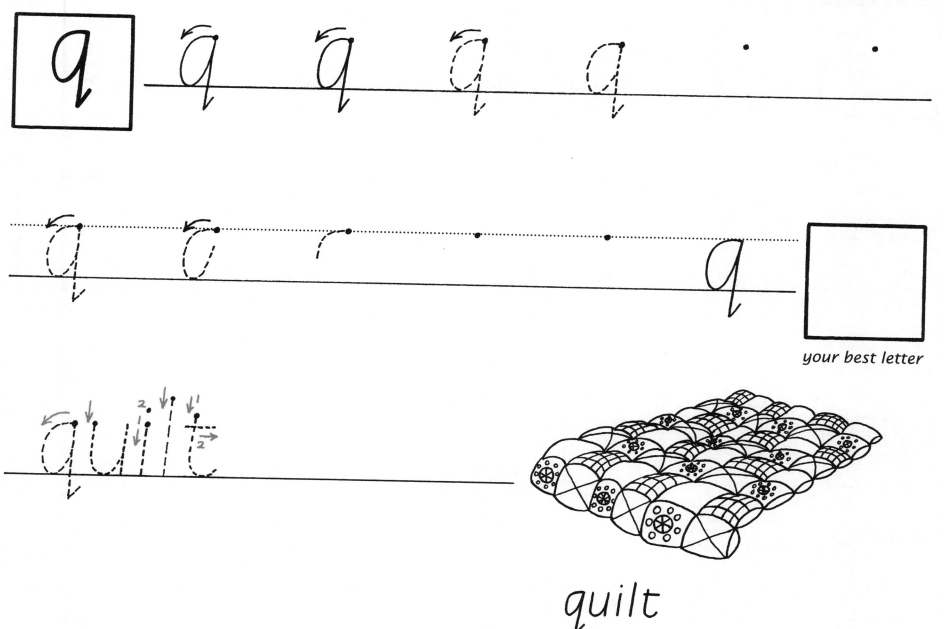

your best letter

quilt

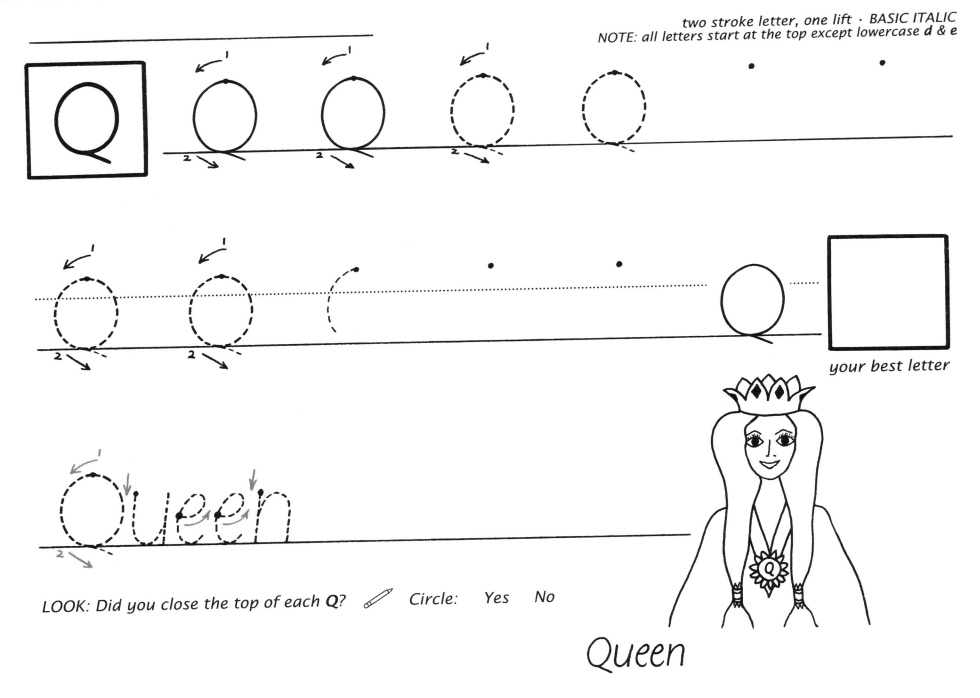

your best letter

LOOK: Did you close the top of each **Q**? ✐ Circle: Yes   No

Queen

one stroke letter, no lift · b, p family · BASIC ITALIC
NOTE: all letters start at the top except lowercase **d & e**

b

b b b b

b

b r i b

your best letter

butterfly

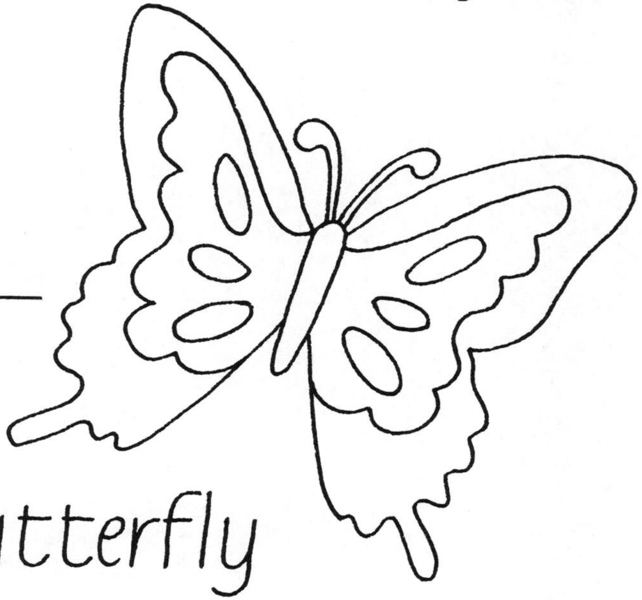

butterfly

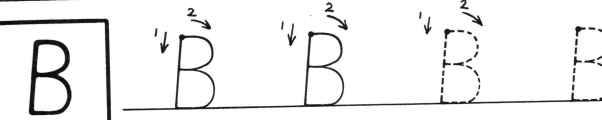

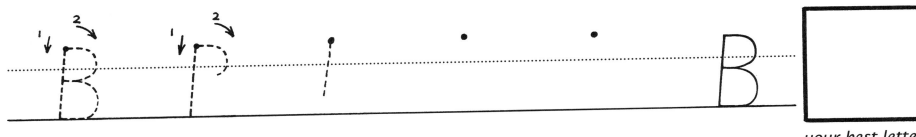

your best letter

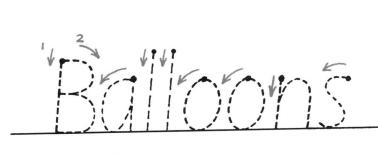

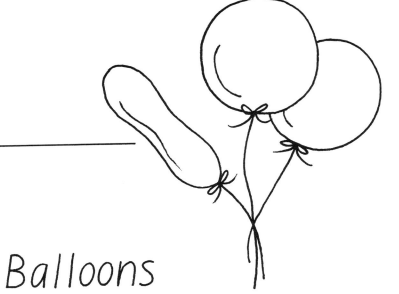

Balloons

your best letter

parrot

your best letter

Peacock

one stroke letter, no lift · o, e, c, s family · BASIC ITALIC
NOTE: all letters start at the top except lowercase **d** & **e**

o

your best letter

octopus

LOOK: Did you close the top of each **o**? ✏ Circle: Yes   No

octopus

NOTE: all letters start at the top except lowercase **d** & **e**

O

your best letter

Octagon

LOOK: Did you close the top of each **O**? Circle: Yes No

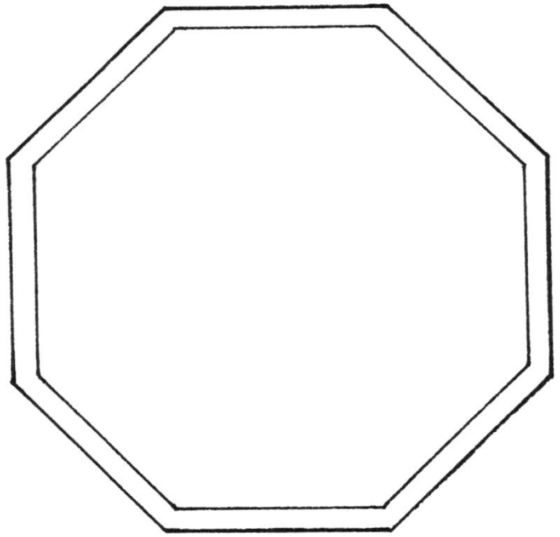

Octagon

one stroke letter, no lift · o, e, c, s family · BASIC ITALIC
NOTE: all letters start at the top except lowercase *d* & *e*

your best letter

LOOK: Did you trace each **e** before writing your own?

Circle: Yes   No

elephant

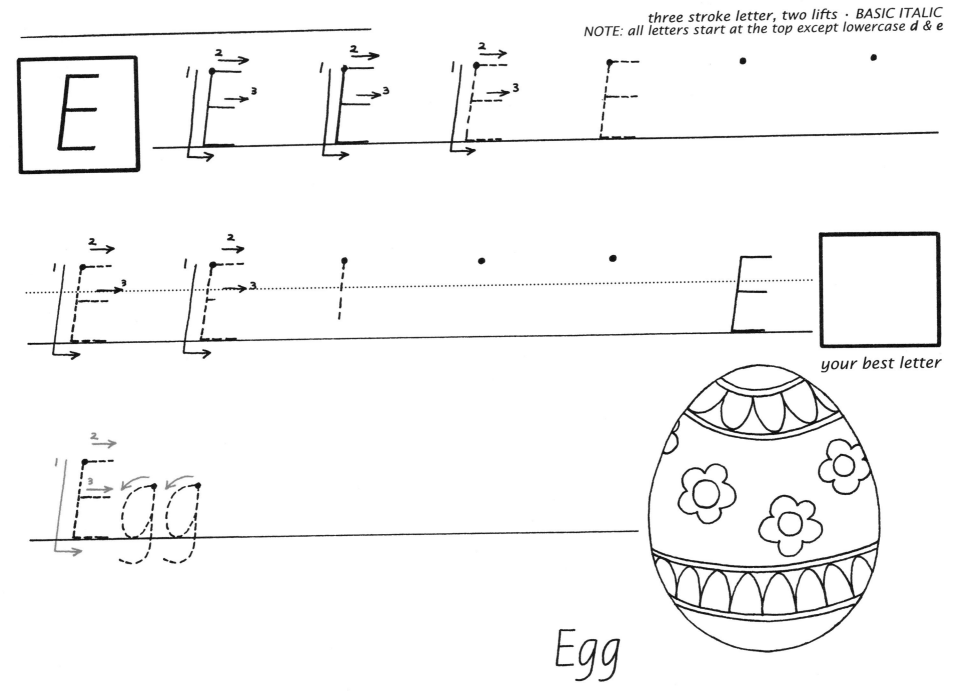

your best letter

Egg

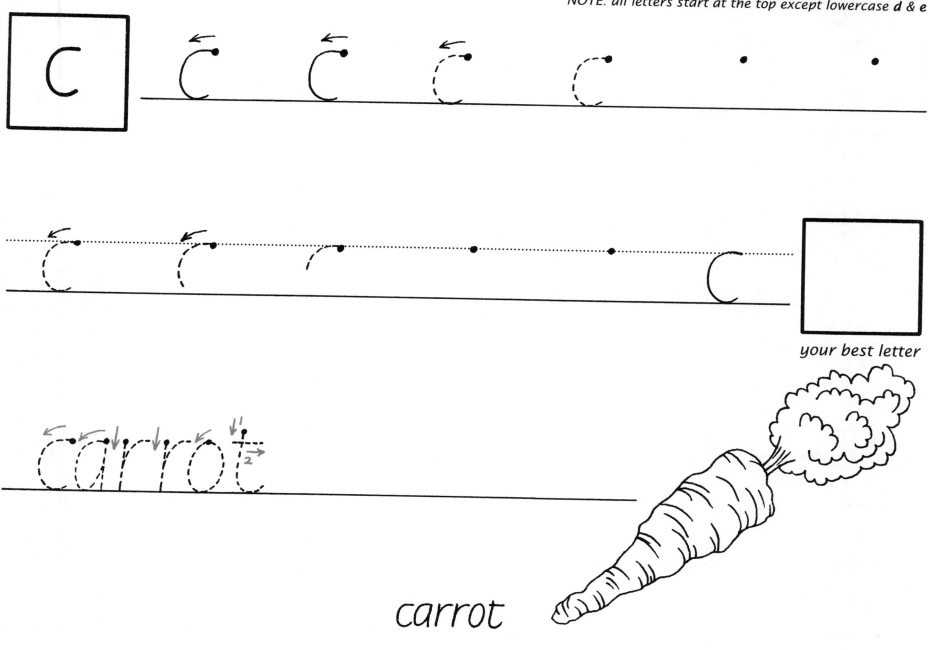

your best letter

carrot

C C C C C C

C C C C C

your best letter

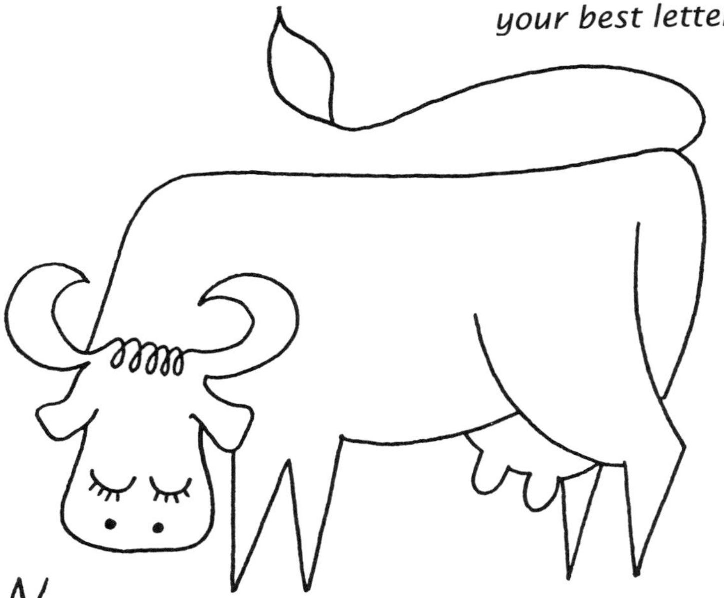

Cow

LOOK: Did you trace each letter before writing your own?

✎ Circle: Yes   No

Cow

36

one stroke letter, no lift · *o, e, c, s* family · BASIC ITALIC
NOTE: all letters start at the top except lowercase **d** & **e**

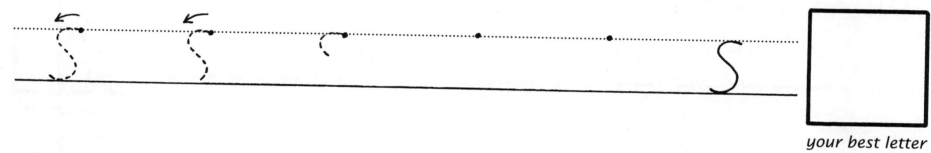

your best letter

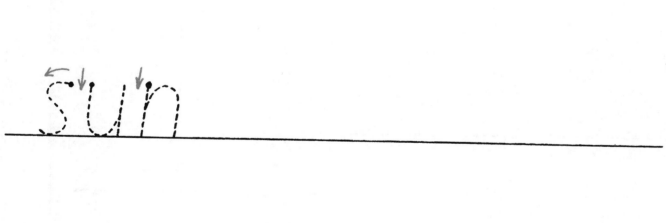

sun

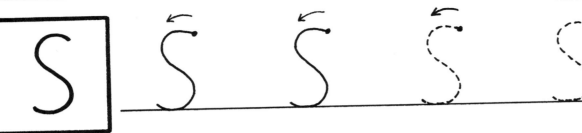

S S S S

S S S S

your best letter

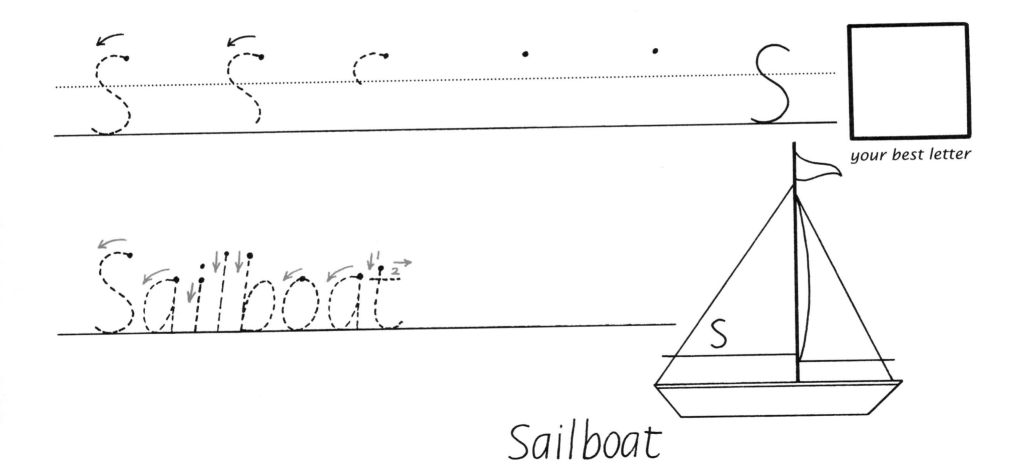

Sailboat

Sailboat

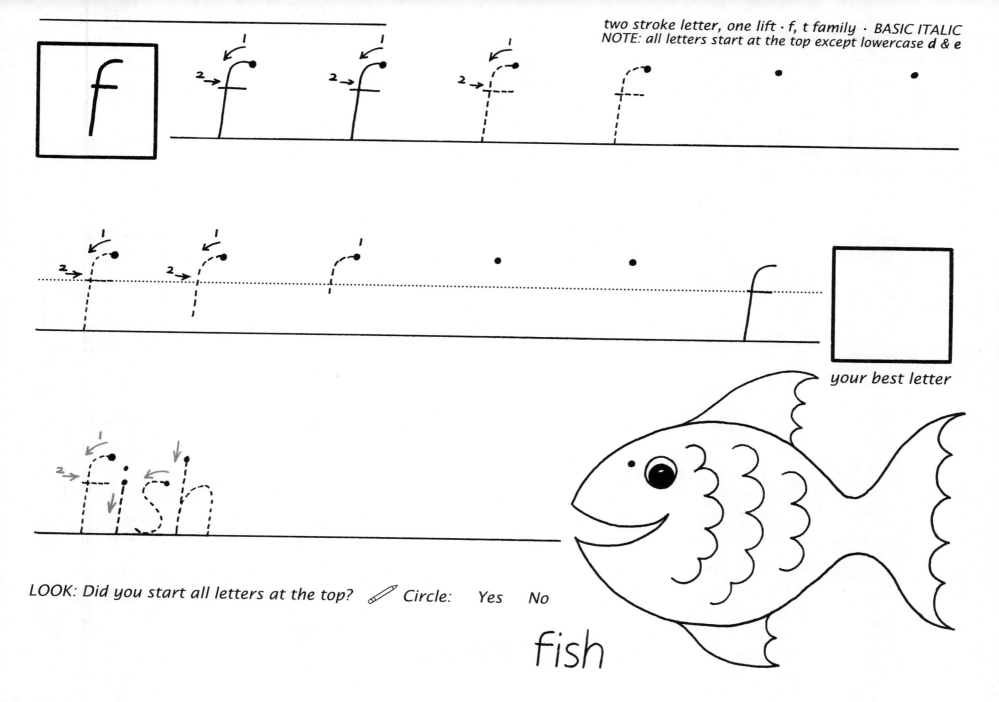

f

your best letter

LOOK: Did you start all letters at the top? ✏ Circle: Yes   No

fish

© 2012 Getty-Dubay

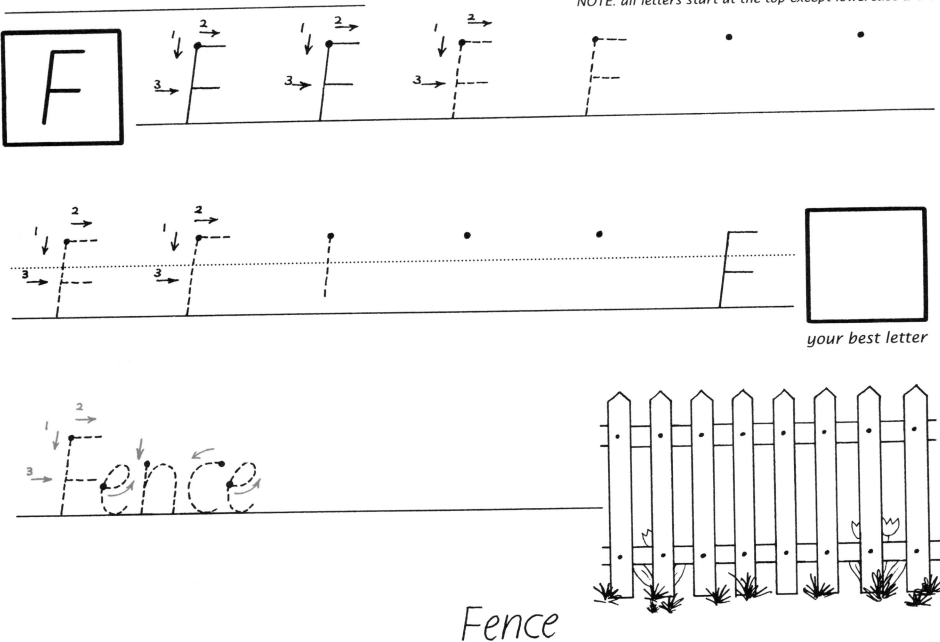

your best letter

Fence

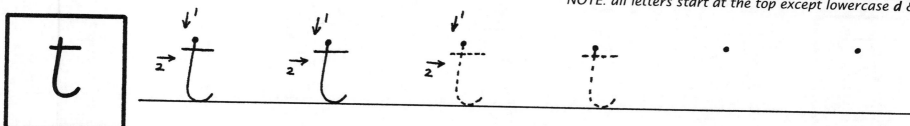

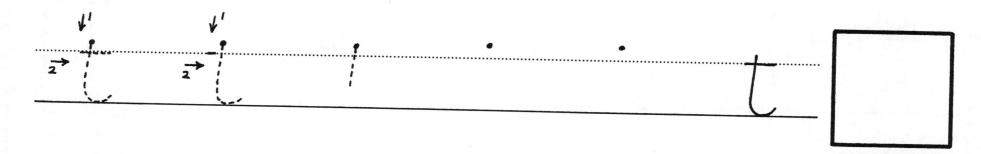

your best letter

turkey

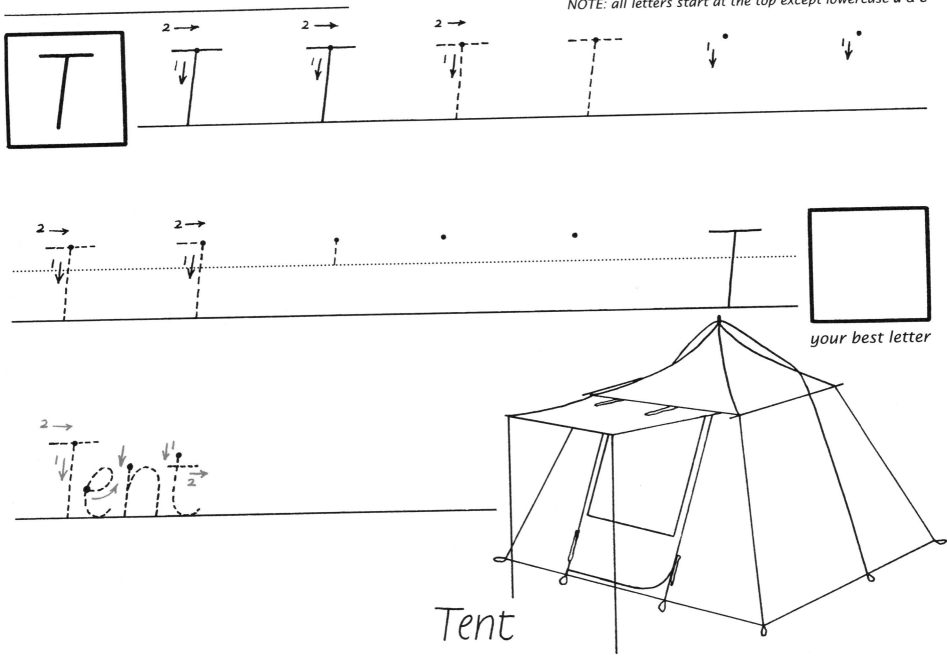

your best letter

Tent

one stroke numeral · no lift

zero

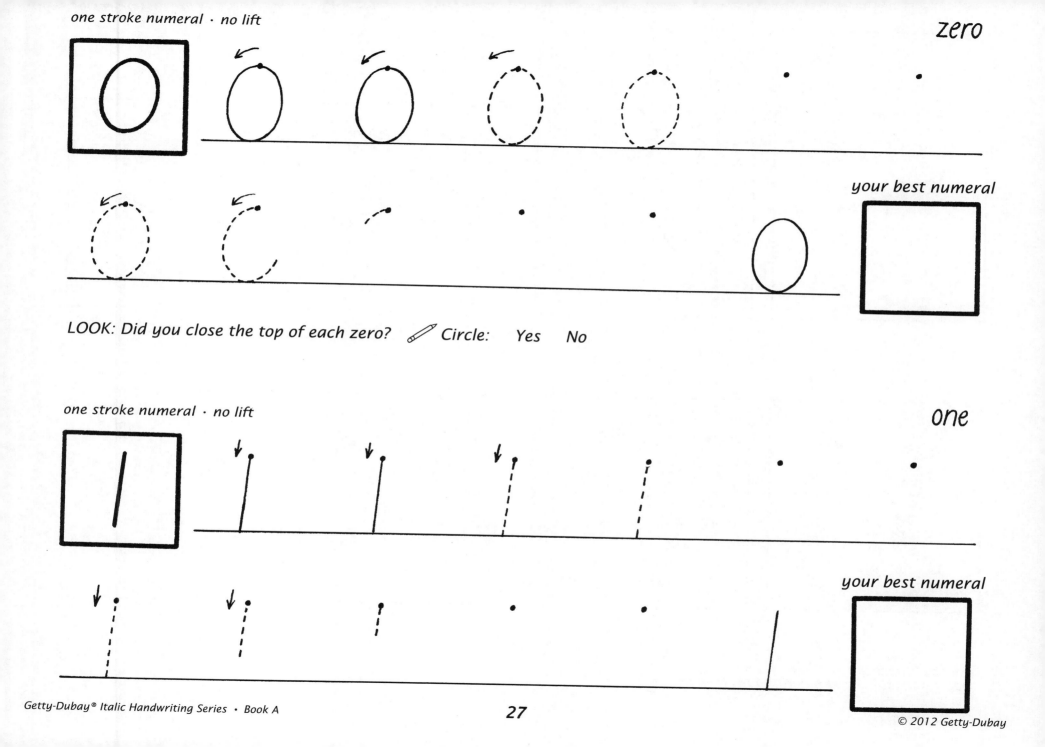

your best numeral

LOOK: Did you close the top of each zero? Circle: Yes   No

one stroke numeral · no lift

one

your best numeral

© 2012 Getty-Dubay

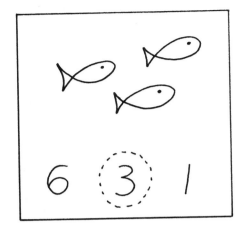

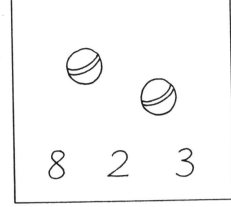

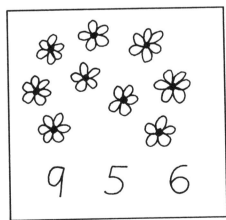

Ask the student to circle the numeral
that stands for the number of objects in the box.

32

Getty-Dubay® Italic Handwriting Series · Book A

one stroke numeral · no lift

two

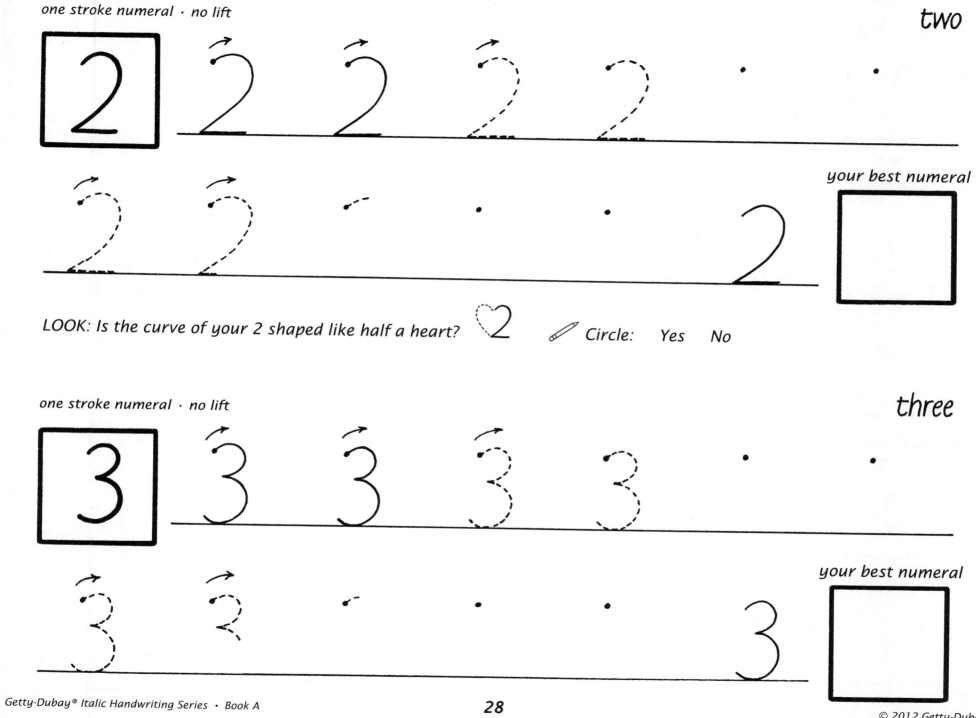

your best numeral

LOOK: Is the curve of your 2 shaped like half a heart?   Circle: Yes   No

one stroke numeral · no lift

three

your best numeral

eight

one stroke numeral · no lift

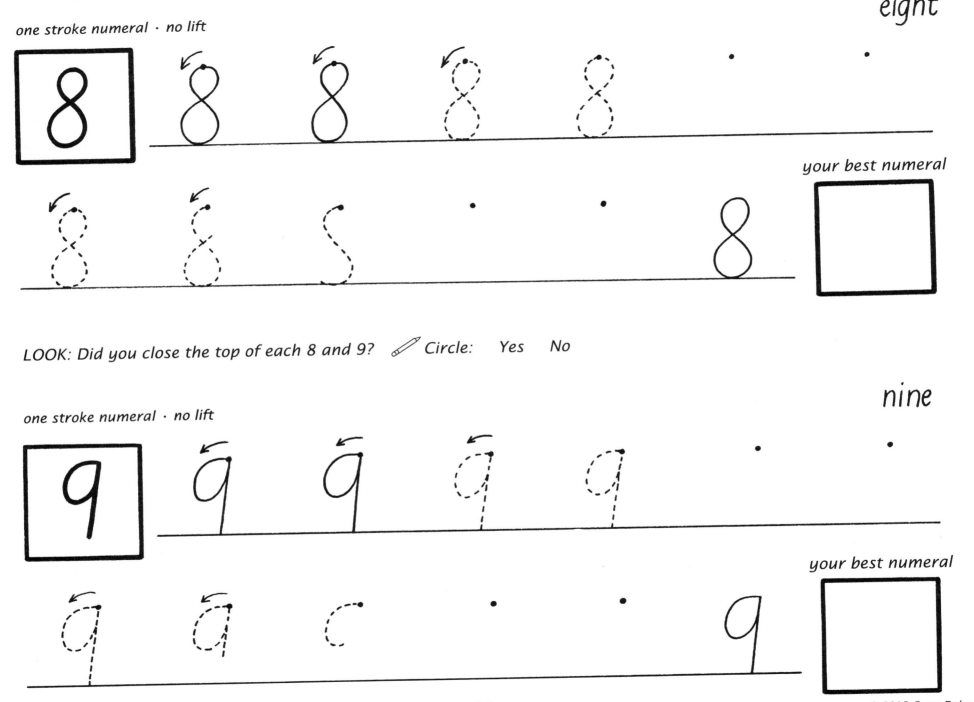

your best numeral

LOOK: Did you close the top of each 8 and 9? 🖉 Circle: Yes   No

nine

one stroke numeral · no lift

your best numeral

Getty-Dubay® Italic Handwriting Series · Book A

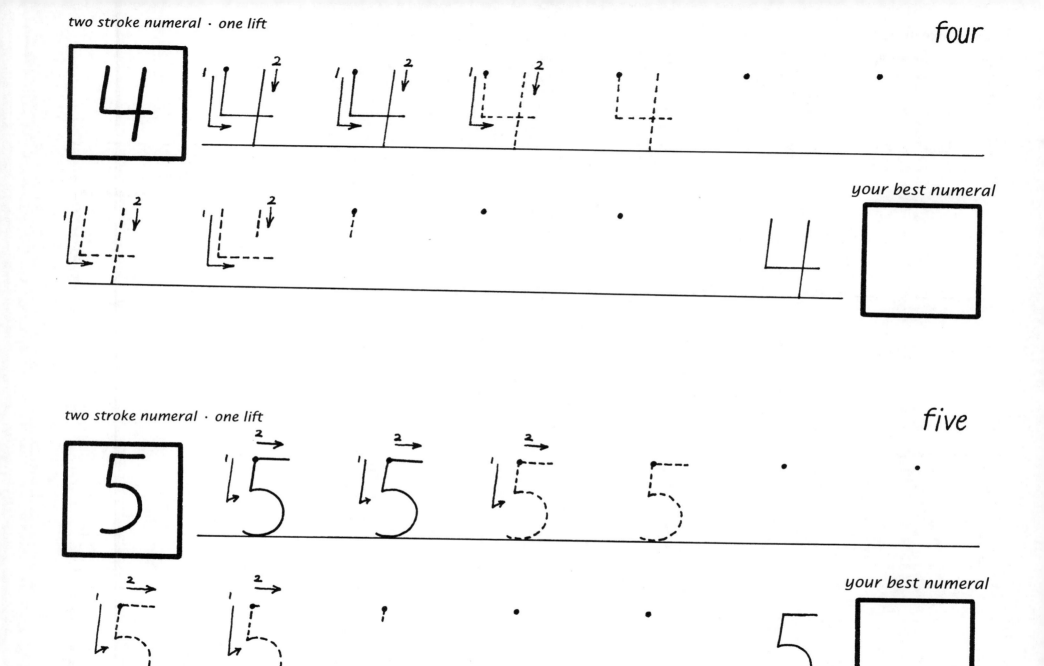

two stroke numeral · one lift

four

your best numeral

two stroke numeral · one lift

five

your best numeral

one stroke numeral · no lift

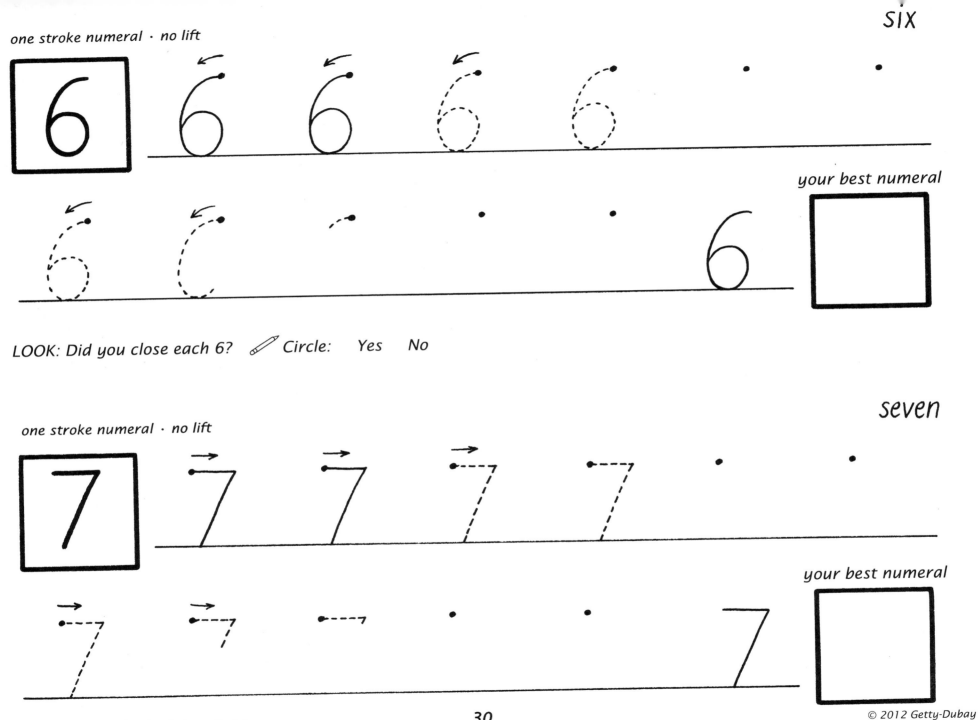

your best numeral

LOOK: Did you close each 6? Circle: Yes   No

seven

one stroke numeral · no lift

your best numeral

Getty-Dubay® Italic Handwriting Series · Book A

© 2012 Getty-Dubay